Algrove Publishing Limited
36 Mill Street, P.O. Box 1238
Almonte, Ontario, Canada K0A 1A0

Telephone: (613) 256-0350
Fax: (613) 256-0360
Email: sales@algrove.com
Web: www.algrove.com

Library and Archives Canada Cataloguing in Publication

Thomas Burdett (Firm)
    Hotel and saloon supplies / Thomas Burdett.

(Classic reprint series)
Reprint of the catalogue published Montreal : T. Burdett, 1904. Includes
original t.p.
Includes index.
ISBN 978-1-897030-71-4

    1. Hotels--Furniture, equipment, etc.--Catalogs. 2. Bars (Drinking
establishments)--Equipment and supplies--Catalogs. 3. Thomas Burdett
(Firm)--Catalogs. I. Title. II. Series: Classic reprint series (Almonte, Ont.)

TX912.T48 2009   647.94'029   C2009-900594-8

Printed in Canada
#1-8-09

Publisher's Note

Although this is a Canadian catalogue (hence the spelling catalogue, not catalog), it is a mixture of both Canadian and American content. The American content is most obvious in the toasts (pp 261 to 281) but this is common in catalogues from the 1800s and early 1900s. In those days copyright was not enforced as rigidly as is now the case. Catalogues were frequently constructed from a mixture of original material and whatever images and text that could be lifted from other publications.

Regardless of the extent of this plagiarism, the catalogue represents what was current in bar fixtures and supplies in North America in that era.

Leonard G. Lee, Publisher
Almonte, Ontario
August 2009

How We Make Our Books - *You may not have noticed, but this book is quite different from other softcover books you might own. The vast majority of paperbacks, whether mass-market or the more expensive trade paperbacks, have the pages sheared and notched at the spine so that they may be glued together. The paper itself is often of newsprint quality. Over time, the paper will brown and the spine will crack if flexed. Eventually the pages fall out.*

All of our softcover books, like our hardcover books, have sewn bindings. The pages are sewn in signatures of sixteen or thirty-two pages and these signatures are then sewn to each other. They are also glued at the back but the glue is used primarily to hold the cover on, not to hold the pages together.

There is one more thing you will note about this book as you read it; it opens easily and does not require constant hand pressure to keep it open. In all but the smallest sizes, our books will also lie open on a table, something that a book bound only with glue will never do unless you have broken its spine.

The cost of these extras is well below their value and while we do not expect a medal for incorporating them, we did want you to notice them.

ESTABLISHED 1892

THOMAS BURDETT

MONTREAL, Canada

Hotel and Saloon Supplies

Carbonating Machinery

1904

Algrove Publishing
Classic Reprint Series

I AM AGENT FOR.....

The Cleveland Faucet Co.

I carry in stock the following:

Champion Beer Pumps,
　　Monitor Hydraulic Beer Pumps,
　　　　Champion Carbonic Gas Regulators,
　　　　　　Bar Faucets,
　　　　　　　　Hand Pumps,
　　　　　　　　　　Picnic Beer Pumps,
　　　　　　　　　　　　Ice and Coil Boxes,
　　　　　　　　　　　　　　Novelty Boxes,
　　　　　　　　　　　　　　　　Workboards,
　　　　　　　　　　　　　　　　　　Lunch Coolers,

Beer Pump Supplies,
　　Glass Ware of every description,
　　　　Carbonic Acid Gas,
　　　　　　Hot Water Heaters,
　　　　　　　　Soda Fountains and Supplies,
　　　　　　　　　　Crushed Fruits,

———

I carry everything pertaining to the Beer and Soda Fountain, Supplies and Fixtures.

———

I also do all kinds of Repairing and Setting Up of Beer Pumps, Work Boards and Soda Fountains.

———

If you have any work to be done I will guarantee to give satisfaction, and my charges will be moderate.

———

GIVE US A CALL

Thomas Burdett

To Saloon Keepers

IN PLACING BEFORE YOU MY NINTH ANNUAL CATALOGUE, I wish to call your attention to my extensive experience in Saloon Fitting. For twelve years I have been engaged in this line of business, fitting up almost all the first-class Saloons in Montreal and all over Canada, and that my work is satisfactory is proven by my steady retention of this business. ∴　∴　∴　∴　∴

My prices are no higher than consistent with first-class work ; experience will teach any saloon keeper that second-class goods are expensive at any price, as they cause endless trouble. ∴　∴

Hoping to be favored with any inquiries or orders you may have in this line, I am,

Respectfully yours,

THOMAS BURDETT

OFFICE AND SHOW ROOMS :
290 ST. PAUL ST.   -   MONTREAL

GOODS ENTRANCE AND BONDED WAREHOUSE:
131 COMMISSIONERS ST. - MONTREAL

How we do Business

 **I**N order to facilitate the handling of a large business, it is absolutely necessary that strict rules be enforced, which result to the benefit of both buyer and seller, for prompt shipments are then effected which is one of the many important advantages.

We endeavor to reduce expenses to a minimum by avoiding the use of the costly red tape systems in vogue in other establishments, and we therefore kindly ask our customers to help us by following our different instructions covering the sending of orders.

C. O. D. Shipments

We will **Positively** ship no goods C.O.D. unless sufficient Cash accompanies order to guarantee transportation charges.

C. O. D. Orders

Where parties order goods shipped C.O.D. they generally overlook the fact that it would be quite a saving to them to remit full amount of purchase, for all express Companies and Banks charge for the collection and return of money, which expense must be borne by the purchaser.

On Freight Orders give name of Bank to whom you prefer Bill of Lading sent or name of Express Company.

Do not overlook following our terms on C. O. D. shipments, explained on these pages, in order to insure prompt delivery.

How to Order

In ordering **do not fail to sign your name and address,** writing both as plainly as possible. We are compelled to hold many orders because **customers fail to sign their names** and only when they send in a complaint concerning non-arrival of goods are we able to discover their identity. Address should always include City or Town and County. This will avoid delay, not only in entering your order, but also in expediting delivery by transportation company.

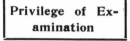

**Our Terms are
Strictly Cash
Ten Days' Time**

To parties of unquestionable respon-sibility we will ship goods on ten days' time. Those desiring to avail themselves of this accommodation, which is offered for the purpose of affording purchasers opportunity of examining goods prior to making payment, are obliged to favor us with satisfactory refer-ences. Accounts not paid in ten days are subject to draft with exchange without notice. Customers would confer a favor upon us by remitting at maturity of invoice, saving themselves the cost of exchange and saving us the unnecessary clerical work which a draft involves.

**Privilege of Ex-
amination**

It is unsatisfactory to both sender and purchaser to unpack fragile merchan-dise at Express office or Freight depot on account of the great risk assumed in the repacking—in consequence of which we **do not ship privilege of examination.**

We guarantee every article as represented.

We cheerfully accept back goods not as ordered, and ex-change those that are unsatisfactory.

Remittances

Do not send Currency in letters which are not registered. It is not safe and we strongly advise against it. It is preferable to send Postal Notes, Express Money Orders and Bank Drafts which can be secured everywhere at nominal cost, and are payable only to the firm in whose favor they are drawn ; in this way remittances can be sent safely in an ordinary unregistered letter.

Private Checks are sent for collection, and shipments delayed until returns are received.

Stamps Accepted in all denominations and in any amount.

Do not destroy this catalogue by tearing or cutting out illustrations. Article and lot number are sufficient.

DIRECTIONS

Shipping

All our shipments are F. O. B. Montreal. We make no charge for package or cartage.

Always state just how you wish goods shipped, whether by freight or express, otherwise we assume that our discretion is to be used. It is important that you specify how we should ship, as we have no means of knowing if you are in a great hurry for goods and wish them rushed by express, or if you can wait and thereby take advantage of the lower freight rates.

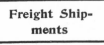

Mail Shipments

Glassware and Fluids cannot be sent through the mails. We will not send goods by mail unless postage is included in remittance. Unregistered mail shipments are unsatisfactory on account of the large percentage which go astray and are lost. We advise registration, for which include 5 cents in addition to amount of postage ; this will insure delivery. We will not hold ourselves responsible for shipments ordered sent by mail unregistered.

If you are not sure as to the weight of the article, be sure to enclose enough money for postage ; if you send too much **we will refund balance.**

Express Shipments

Give us name of Express Company you prefer.

If no Express office in your town specify nearest shipping point.

All collections covering C. O. D. shipment by Express, are made by the Express Company and there is a charge for this service which must be borne by the customer.

Freight Shipments

We are not the best judges as to which Railroad gives you the most prompt delivery, therefore it is to your interest to specify name of the preferred company.

If there is no freight depot or express office at your point, the charges must be prepaid. When this is the case, include sufficient in your remittance to cover such charges, otherwise your shipment will be held until we write you and receive the money.

Full remittance including freight charges must be made with orders for towns without agent at station.

We ship C. O. D. by Freight, providing sufficient money accompanies order to guarantee acceptance and to show your good faith. Collection is made by draft with Bills of Lading attached drawn through your local bank. Upon payment of draft the Bill of Lading will be surrendered to you and for which the freight agent will deliver the shipment.

If goods do not reach you within reasonable time, advise us and we shall send tracer, which usually quickly locates the missing shipment, or hurries along the slow one.

We furnish Bills of Lading upon request covering all freight shipments, and we endeavor in every case to secure the lowest possible freight rates. After shipments are delivered to transportation company and we hold their receipt for same in good order our responsability ceases. If shipment is not delivered, you must look to the carrier for reimbursement.

We will be glad to make the claim on the companies for you and aid you in every possible way to collect it, but **remittances for goods shipped must be made to us in full.**

Correspondence

We have a finely equipped and well organized Correspondence department, the services of which you can command at all times. Do not hesitate to inquire concerning anything which is not entirely clear to you. Our correspondents will go into detail cheerfully.

If there is any article which you desire and is not listed by us we will exert our utmost endeavor to secure same for you at the lowest market price.

Mistakes

Mistakes are liable to happen—no one is infallible. If an error is made, give us a chance to correct it. Write us fully so that the matter can be intelligently investigated and rectified. Some people are hasty in their conclusions and say nothing, thus not giving us a chance to set the matter right ; this is an injustice to us as we lose their good will. We treat our customers as we wish to be treated.

Returning Goods to us

Return no goods unless you receive our consent as we may give you shipping directions other than to our address.

We are pleased to accept back anything not satisfactory in exchange for other goods, providing return charges are paid by you. If an error is made by us we pay transportation charges and will give shipping instructions immediately on receipt of your letter.

Do not return goods by express weighing over 20 lbs.

Do not forget to mark your name and address on packages so we may know who it is from when received as it is almost impossible to identify goods otherwise.

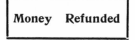

When returning glassware pack same very carefully. Glassware received back in broken condition in consequence of poor packing will not be credited. Where parties remit in excess of the amount of their purchase refund is made immediately.

Should we be unable to furnish the kind of goods ordered on account of being sold out of the particular item, refund is made promptly together with information advising when we will again have goods wanted or calling attention to a similar item.

Should goods prove unsatisfactory, do not hesitate to advise us and we will instruct as to their disposition. Refund in cash, or exchange of goods will be promptly made. However, do not return any goods until you have advised us so that we can give you the proper shipping instructions.

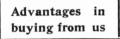

We employ none but the most Experienced Packers and great care and attention is given to this department of our business. Positively no goods are allowed to leave our shipping room unless in perfect condition. If handled with ordinary care, our packages will reach you in good order. Transportation Companies are responsible for excessive breakage caused through careless handling.

Advantages in buying from us

All previous prices are invalidated by those given in this catalogue. Those quoted in this catalogue remain in force until our next issue, unless a reduction in values takes place, in which case a corresponding refund will be made. In all instances we give our customer every advantage possible, which is a well known fact to our regular trade.

Do not destroy this catalogue by tearing or cutting out illustrations. The article and lot number are sufficient.

" The U. S. Modern " Cork Puller No. 3

With Wooden Knob Handle.

A Favorite where used.

Comprises all the points embrased in the regular Modern, as illustrated and described on the next page.

Price, each ....$ 3.50

Write for discount.

The " Modern " Cork Puller

The Mechanical Wonder of the Age

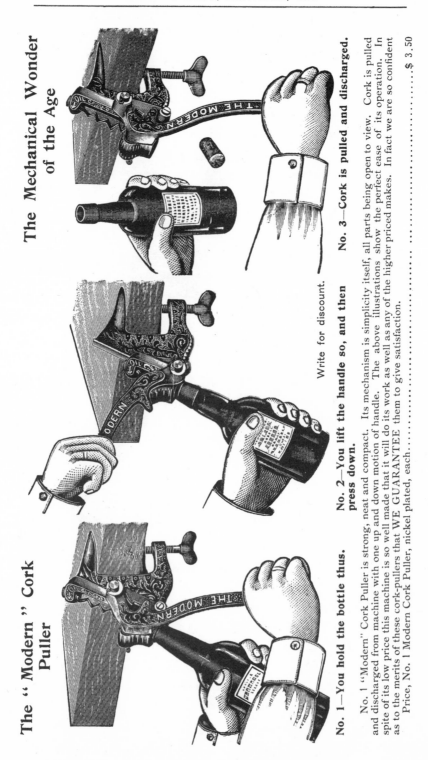

No. 1—You hold the bottle thus.

No. 2—You lift the handle so, and then press down.

No. 3—Cork is pulled and discharged.

Write for discount.

No. 1 "Modern" Cork Puller is strong, neat and compact. Its mechanism is simplicity itself, all parts being open to view. Cork is pulled and discharged from machine with one up and down motion of handle. The above illustrations show the perfect ease of its operation. In spite of its low price this machine is so well made that it will do its work as well as any of the higher priced makes. In fact we are so confident as to the merits of these cork-pullers that WE GUARANTEE them to give satisfaction.

Price, No. 1 Modern Cork Puller, nickel plated, each............$ 3.50

PRICE LIST

OF

U. S. Modern Cork Puller Parts

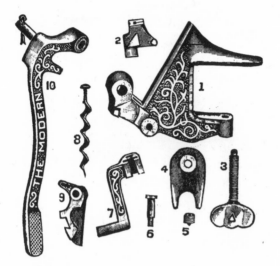

Price, No.	1—Body	....	$1.00
"	2—Nut	....	.50
"	3—Clamp Screw	....	.15
"	4—Clamp Washer	....	.10
"	5—Cap Screw	....	.10
"	6—Lever Screw	....	.10
"	7—Cross Head	....	.25
"	8—Worm or Screw	....	.50
"	9—Frog or Catch	....	.25
"	10—Lever	....	.80

Write for discount.

The Champion Cork Puller and Re=Corker

With Latest Improved Bottle=Holding Clamp

A SURE WINNER

NEAT,
SIMPLE,
STRONG,
COMPACT,
DURABLE,
WARRANTED

A QUICK,
SURE
PULLER,
A SAFE AND
EFFECTIVE
RE - CORKER.

Especially adapted for use in Hotels, Bar Rooms, Clubs, Restaurants, or wherever a Stationary Puller can be used.

THE CHAMPION is abreast of the times and away ahead of all competitors. Will quickly and safely draw the cork from any bottle, and as rapidly recork the bottle after part of contents have been used, a feature highly appreciated by all users. Guaranteed to give perfect satisfaction. Weight complete, six pounds ; height above counter when set up, five inches. The frame is finely engraved in handsome designs. The worm and other working parts are made of best grades of oil-tempered steel, and warranted to stand the work.

Don't overlook the re-corking feature.

Price, Full Nickel Plated, each $3.50

Write for discount.

PRICE LIST

OF

Champion Cork Puller Parts

MANUFACTURED BY

ARCADE MANUFACTURING CO.,   -   Freeport, Ill., U.S.A.

1897 Pattern

Price, No. 1—Right Frame...$ 1.00
"   2—Left Frame....................................... .75
"   3—Left Bottle Clamp .... .30
"   4—Right Bottle Clamp............................... .30
"   5—Upper Nut....... .... .25
"   6—Brass Washer.................................... .10
"   7—Lower Nut....................................... .25
"   8—Rocker Arm .... .10
"   9—Lifting Hook.................................... .10
"   10—Clamp Washer .... .10
"   11-12—Rubber Cushions (pair)...... .... .15
"   13—Connecting Link .... .10
"   14—Wire Stripper .... .10
"   15—Steel Spring .... .10
"   16—Wood Handle .... .10
"   17—Operating Lever .... .80
"   18—Worm and Screw................................ .50
"   19—Thumb Screw.................................. .20

In ordering give number of part wanted.

Write for discount.

Do not Wait Until You Cut Your Hands.

The Yankee Cork Puller

absolutely without effort draws all corks for a lifetime. It cannot get lost. Attached anywhere—-sideboard, icebox, door frame or wall. Corks, if desired, may be drawn ONLY part way, to be removed later by the fingers.

No Woman, Wife or Servant, should be allowed to Struggle with a Corkscrew.

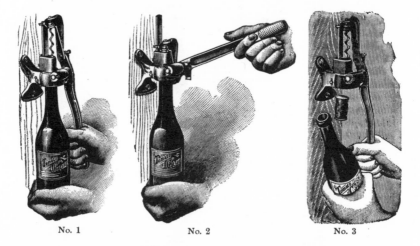

No. 1   No. 2   No. 3

No. 1—The bottle is held in place as shown—the handle down.

No. 2—Raise the handle as shown and the screw automatically enters the cork.

No. 3—Lower the handle and the cork is not only drawn but also automatically discharged from the machine.

Reflect on your exasperating hunt for a corkscrew ; the twisting into the cork ; the hard tug and the great danger. Remember the broken off cork in the neck, and the bits left in the bottle, and don't forget those unspoken "cusses".

Think of the great number of household bottles to be opened—Catsup, Oil, Pickle, Olive, Flavoring Extract, Medicine and——well the other bottles, and decide to own a YANKEE and you will

SETTLE THIS PROBLEM FOR A LIFETIME.

The " YANKEE " is beautifully finished and is indestructible. Price, nickel plated...$ 2.60

Write for discount.

The No. 2 "Yankee" Cork Puller

For use of Saloons, Restaurants, Soda Fountains, Etc.

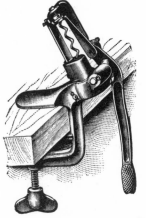

A short up-and-down movement of the handle draws the tightest cork, and automatically discharges it.

A few of its many advantages over the **old-fashioned** cork-pullers are :

That a cork may be drawn exactly as desired, either **entirely out** or simply **part way,** and the handle never moves back over the counter to occupy valuable space.

All wearing parts **are made of steel** and **not** cast-iron. The business parts **slide** on a **polished steel track** instead of being **enclosed** in a rough cast-iron tube.

Every part is in plain sight, **there are no insides** to clog up and get out of order.

Its smoothly finished surface gives a rich appearance and is easily **kept clean,** as it has **no** decorated surface to **catch the dirt** and **to rust.**

A new corkscrew can be put into the Yankee, in a moment, by a child ; heretofore this has required a kit of tools, hours time, an expert mechanic, considerable patience, and plenty of luck.

Price, nickel plated $3.25

Price List of Yankee Cork Puller Parts

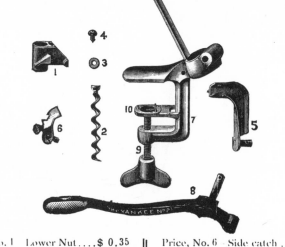

Price, No. 1	Lower Nut....$ 0.35	Price, No. 6	Side catch ....$ 0.25
" 2	Worm screw.. .50	" 7	Body 2.00
" 3	Iron washer... .05	" 8	Lever 1.00
" 4	Top nut plunger .10	" 9	Thumb screw . .30
" 5	Plunger ...... .25	" 10	Clamp washer. .20

Write for discount.

Walker's Quick and Easy Cork Puller

Made by Erie Specialty Co., Erie, Pa., U.S.A.

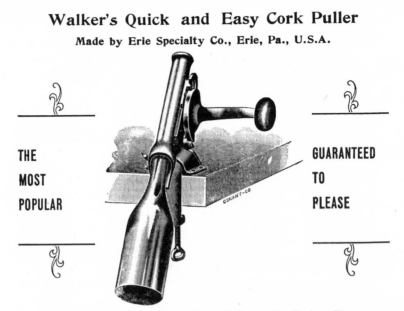

THE

MOST

POPULAR

GUARANTEED

TO

PLEASE

One movement of the Lever forward draws the Cork.   The reverse movement throws the Cork off and places the Lever back in position.

No Injury to Operator.   No Bottles Broken.

Especially adapted for rapid work.   Cuts the wire while pulling the cork. Crown and Seal Lifter Attachment.

Price, each ....$ 3.50

For convenience of Customers in ordering Parts of Puller this list is arranged with Retail Prices of each.

Price, A—Body ....$ 1.00			Price, G—Clamp.......... $0.50		
" B—Lever............ .80			" H—Crown & Seal Lifter .10		
" C—Large Sleeve. .... .40			" K—Bottle Clasp....... .50		
" F—Small Sleeve...... .30			" 30 —Screw .... .50		
" E—Crosshead .... .40			" 30½—Nut .... .50		

Write for discount.

No. 42

Walker's Quick and Easy Lemon Squeezer

1901 Design has no Equal

Patented February 9, 1897.

It has been very much improved by using a glass juice receiver which sets in bottom of outside iron cup. The crusher head and the perforated spiral ribbed crusher cup, holding lemon, are made from cast aluminum. The aluminum cup and glass juice receiver set in loosely, and can instantly be removed for cleaning. The juice of the lemon does not come in contact with the iron metal which insures absolute purity and cleanliness.

The Squeezer combines a squeezing, rotating movement, which is adjusted so that it extracts every particle of juice, making it the most economical Squeezer made, and Quick and Easy to operate.

Price, each ....$ 5.75

Packed singly in wood box ; for shipping one-half dozen, in case.

Measurement, 20¾ x 15¾ x 12¾ ins. Gross weight, 88 lbs. ; net weight, 67 lbs.

NEW STYLE

Walker's Quick and Easy Lemon Squeezer

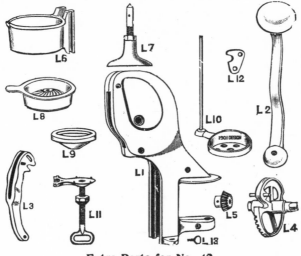

Extra Parts for No. 42

For convenience in ordering repair parts, this list is arranged with retail price of each.

L 1—Body, each	$ 2.00
L 2—Lever, each	.50
L 3—Link, each	.50
L 4—Large Gear, each	.50
L 5—Small Gear, each	.20
L 6—Iron Cup Holder, each	.50
L 7—Aluminum Crusher, each	.80
L 8—Aluminum Strainer Cup, each	1.00
L 9—Glass receiver, each	.10
L 10—Glass holder, each	.30
L 11—Thumb-screw for Clamp, each	.30
L 12—Dog, each	.10
L 13—Thumb-screw for glass holder, each	.10

Write for discount.

OLD STYLE

Quick and Easy Lemon Squeezer Parts

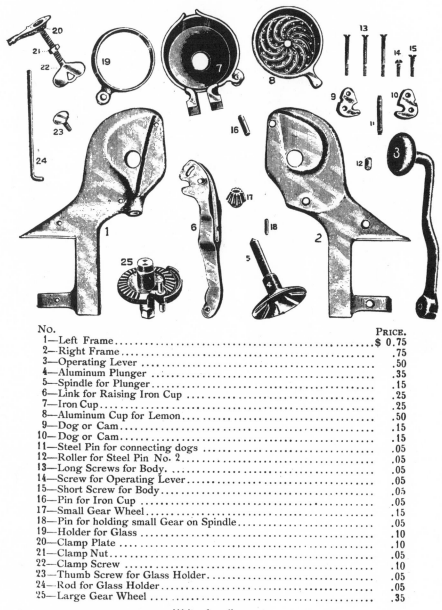

No.		Price.
1—Left Frame		$ 0.75
2—Right Frame		.75
3—Operating Lever		.50
4—Aluminum Plunger		.35
5—Spindle for Plunger		.15
6—Link for Raising Iron Cup		.25
7—Iron Cup		.25
8—Aluminum Cup for Lemon		.50
9—Dog or Cam		.15
10—Dog or Cam		.15
11—Steel Pin for connecting dogs		.05
12—Roller for Steel Pin No. 2		.05
13—Long Screws for Body		.05
14—Screw for Operating Lever		.05
15—Short Screw for Body		.05
16—Pin for Iron Cup		.05
17—Small Gear Wheel		.15
18—Pin for holding small Gear on Spindle		.05
19—Holder for Glass		.10
20—Clamp Plate		.10
21—Clamp Nut		.05
22—Clamp Screw		.10
23—Thumb Screw for Glass Holder		.05
24—Rod for Glass Holder		.05
25—Large Gear Wheel		.35

Write for discount.

It's the Pride of the Nation

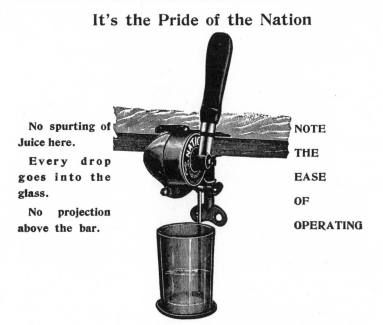

No spurting of Juice here.

Every drop goes into the glass.

No projection above the bar.

NOTE

THE

EASE

OF

OPERATING

CLOSED, LEMON BEING SQUEEZED

It's the only Satisfactory Lemon Squeezer
ON THE MARKET.

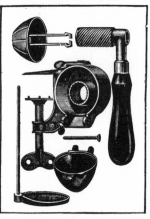

SQUEEZER TAKEN APART

See the perfect mechanical construction and yet so simple that any child can take it apart and put it together in a few seconds.

The only practical Lemon Squeezer for Families, Hotels, Restaurants, Clubs, Saloons, Drug Stores, Hospital, Etc., Etc.

NONE COMPLETE WITHOUT ONE.

Write for discount.

The "National" Lemon Squeezer

Open to receive Lemon.

SOMETHING NEW IN LEMON SQUEEZERS.

At last we have produced a squeezer that is perfect in every detail.

OPERATION.—It is simple. Place lemon in cup, close it up and lock it shut, pull the handle up, which squeezes the lemon without losing a *drop*. The ribbed cone rotates as it enters the lemon, thereby opening cells to facilitate extracting the juice.

CLEANLINESS.—*Only Squeezer* that you can take all apart and put together in five seconds ; simply pull out the hinge pin and the cone, and you have it all apart for cleaning.

PRESSURE.—A large, powerful and quick-acting screw which rotates the ribbed cone as it travels forward into the lemon, thereby extracting all the juice instantaneously.

MATERIAL.—After many years' experimenting, we have produced a special metal that will withstand the corrosive action of the lemon juice. It is very hard, strong and durable.

FINISH.—It's nickel plated and highly polished, with enameled wood handle, shelf, and thumb screws. Packed one in a strong paper box, half dozen in wooden case. Weight, 2½ pounds each.

GUARANTEE.—We guarantee each one to be perfect in workmanship and finish, and will replace any defective parts *free of charge* if delivered to our factory.

Price, each...$ 3.75

Write for discount.

No. 1—The Perfect Lemon Squeezer

Packed for market, one in a wood box, one-half dozen in a substantial wood case.

Price, each $ 3.50

Weight, per dozen, 50 pounds.

Size per case of one dozen 9½ x 7¼ x 14½ inches.

No. 10 — The Perfect Lemon Squeezer

In all respects same as No. 1, except that it is designed to fasten on wall or on ice-box.

Packed for market one each in a wood box, one dozen in a substantial wood case.

Price, each.............$ 3.50

Weight, per dozen, 50 pounds.

Size per case of ½ dozen, 9½ x 7¼ x 14½ inches.

Write for discount.

No. 20—The Perfect Lemon Squeezer

Mounted on wood base and can be moved around as desired.   Designed for family use.

Packed for market one each in a wood box, one dozen in a substantial wood case.

Price, each ....$ 3.50

Weight, per dozen, 50 pounds.

Size of case, ½ dozen, 12⅛ x 10 x 13¾ inches.

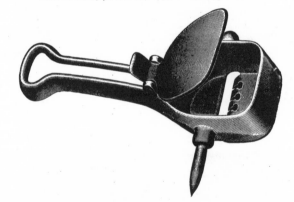

No. 53—Walker's Quick and Easy Ice Shredder
Pick and Hammer Combined

An essential article for the family refrigerators, soda fountains, etc.   The proper thing for making snow balls.   Anti-rust nickel plated.

Price, per dozen...$11.00

No. 53½—Without the Pick

Price, per dozen $10.00

Write for discount.

No. 47—Wood Lemon Squeezer

Made of hard maple highly polished. Nickel hinge. A strong, substantial Squeezer. The proper one for family use, or soda fountains and street stands.

Price, Lignum-Vitae Bowl, per dozen $15.25
Price, Imitation Boxwood Bowl, per dozen......................... 12.50

No. 173 — Walker's Quick and Easy Lime Squeezer.

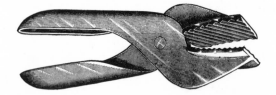

Made of cast aluminum. Will not corrode. Always clean.
Juice absolutely pure.

Price, per dozen $18.50

Write for discount.

No. 37—Walker's Plain Cork Screw

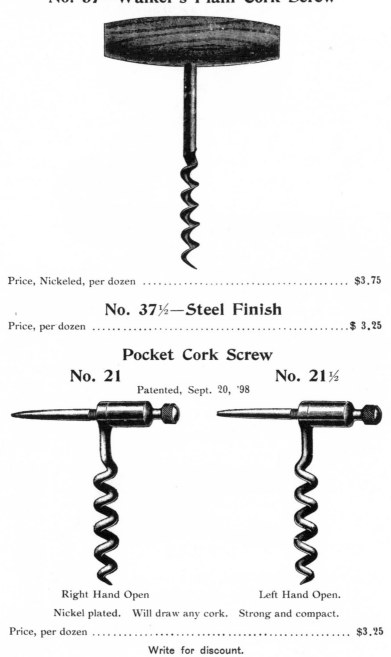

Price, Nickeled, per dozen $3.75

No. 37½—Steel Finish

Price, per dozen .... $ 3.25

Pocket Cork Screw

No. 21   **No. 21½**

Patented, Sept. 20, '98

Right Hand Open   Left Hand Open.

Nickel plated. Will draw any cork. Strong and compact.

Price, per dozen $3.25

Write for discount.

No. 24 — Pocket Cork Screw

Patented Sept. 20, 1898

Nickel plated. Will draw any cork. Made right or left hand. Card etched on head in gross lots and upwards.

Price, per dozen .... $ 3.10

LEFT HAND, No. 24½

Left Hand Pocket Cork Screws, Nos. 20½, 21½ and 24½, are a very compact pocket piece. The left hand Screw is a good joker, therefore makes a nice present and very amusing.

CLOSED

No. 137—Walker's Pocket Cork Screw

With Crown and Seal Opener Handle, in wood tube. Finely nickel plated. Card printed on tube in gross lots and upwards without extra charge.

Price, per dozen .... $ 2.60

Write for discount.

No. 13—Walker's Universal Cork Screw

A universal family Cork Screw. Pulls the smallest and largest corks from any style of bottle. Extra quality of steel. Tempered and tested.

Price, Nickeled, per dozen.....$ 3.10

No. 13½—Steel Finish

Price, per dozen 2.60

No. 23—Walker's Wire Cork Screw

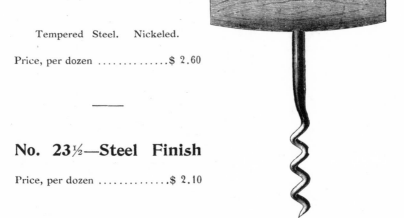

Tempered Steel.   Nickeled.

Price, per dozen ....$ 2.60

No. 23½—Steel Finish

Price, per dozen ....$ 2.10

Write for discount.

WALKER'S CORK SCREWS CARDED

Every Screw tested and guaranteed

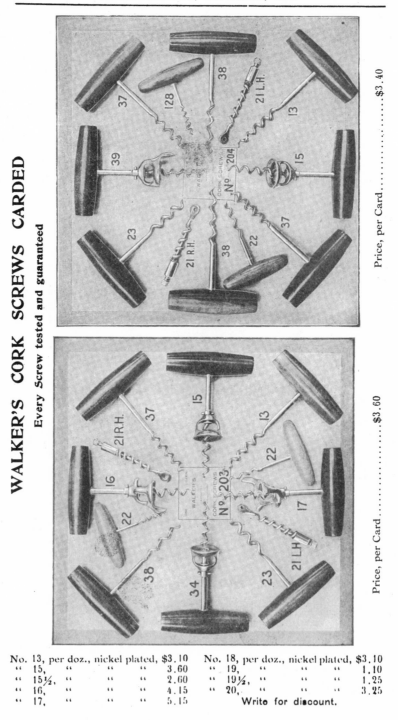

Price, per Card............$3.40

Price, per Card............$3.60

No. 13, per doz., nickel plated, $3.10
" 15,   "   "   "   3.60
" 15½, "   "   "   2.60
" 16,   "   "   "   4.15
" 17,   "   "   "   5.15

No. 18, per doz., nickel plated, $3.10
" 19,   "   "   "   1.10
" 19½, "   "   "   1.25
" 20,   "   "   "   3.25

Write for discount.

WALKER'S CORK SCREWS CARDED

Every Screw tested and guaranteed

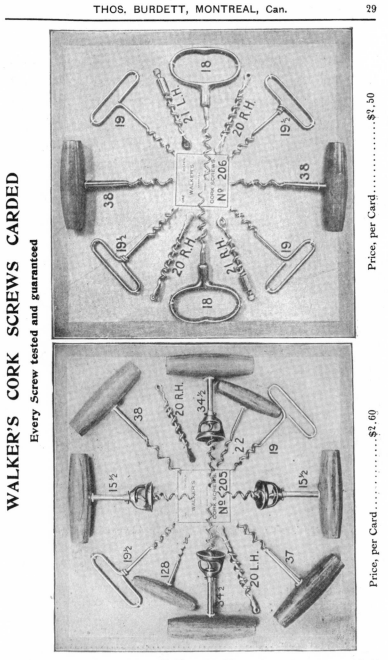

Price, per Card.............$2.50

Price, per Card.............$2.60

No. 21, per doz., nickel plated, $3.25	No. 37, per doz., nickel plated, $3.60
" 22, " " " 1.60	" 38, " " " 3.60
" 23, " " " 2.60	" 39, " " " 5.15
" 34, " " " 4.70	" 128, " " " 2.15
" 34½, " " " 3.10	**Write for discount.**

No. 16—Walker's Universal Self=Pulling Cork Screw

With Crown, Seal and Aluminum Stopper Opener and Wire Cutter.

Patented July 25, 1893, July 14, 1896, March 23, 1897, Aug. 9, 1899, April 17, 1900.

Nickel plated. Every Screw tested. Has no equal. Sells at sight. A household necessity. Pulls all sizes of corks. Every dealer should have it in stock.

Price, per dozen ....$ 4.15

Write for discount.

Acme Round Bowl

Ice Cream, Sherbet and Soda Spoons

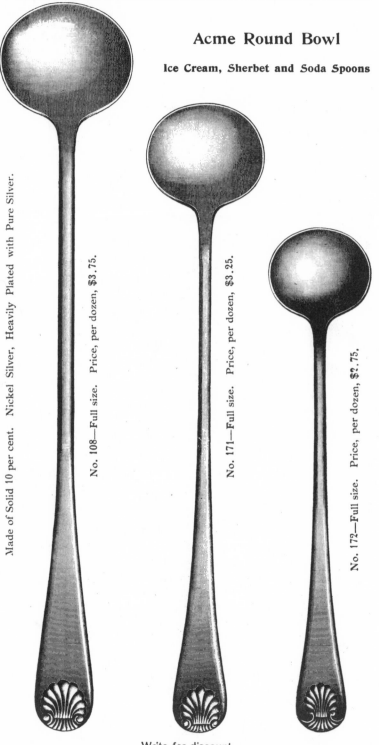

Made of Solid 10 per cent. Nickel Silver, Heavily Plated with Pure Silver.

No. 108—Full size. Price, per dozen, $3.75.

No. 171—Full size. Price, per dozen, $3.25.

No. 172—Full size. Price, per dozen, $2.75.

Write for discount.

BAR SPOONS

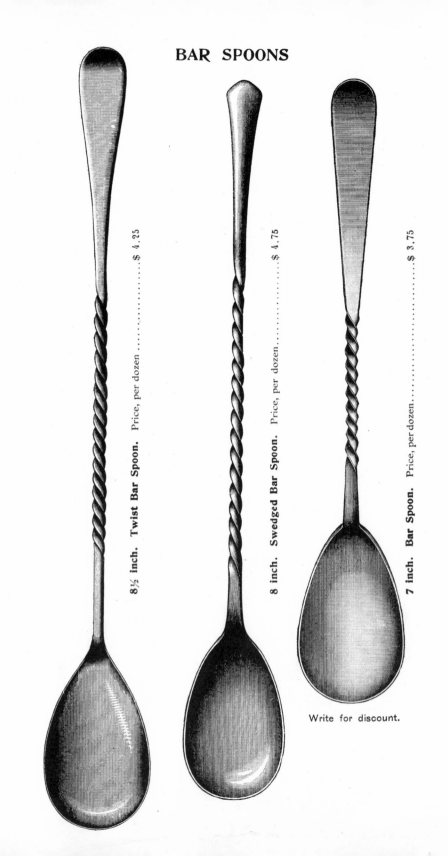

8½ inch. Twist Bar Spoon. Price, per dozen...........$ 4.25

8 inch. Swedged Bar Spoon. Price, per dozen...........$ 4.75

7 inch. Bar Spoon. Price, per dozen...........$ 3.75

Write for discount.

BAR SPOONS   OYSTER FORKS

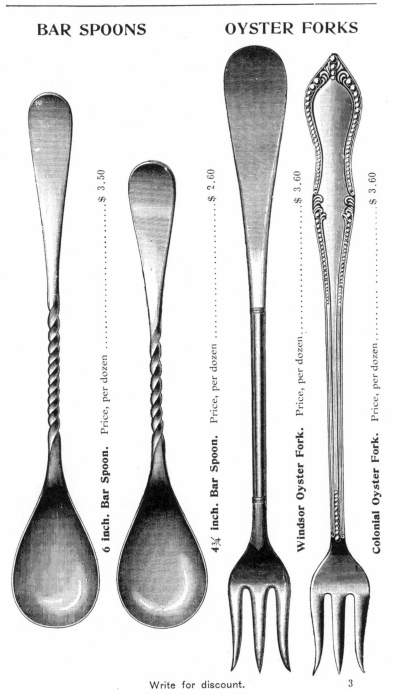

6 inch. Bar Spoon. Price, per dozen ....$ 3.50

4¾ inch. Bar Spoon. Price, per dozen ....$ 2.60

Windsor Oyster Fork. Price, per dozen..........$ 3.60

Colonial Oyster Fork. Price, per dozen..........$ 3.60

Write for discount.   3

Tumbler Holder

Nickel-Plated

Price, No. 1, per dozen $4.50

No. D 79—Silver=Plated Lemon Knife

Price, per dozen $22.00

Lemon Knives

Like cut, per dozen... $7.00
With saw-tooth edge, per dozen................................... 7.75

Write for discount.

MUDDLERS

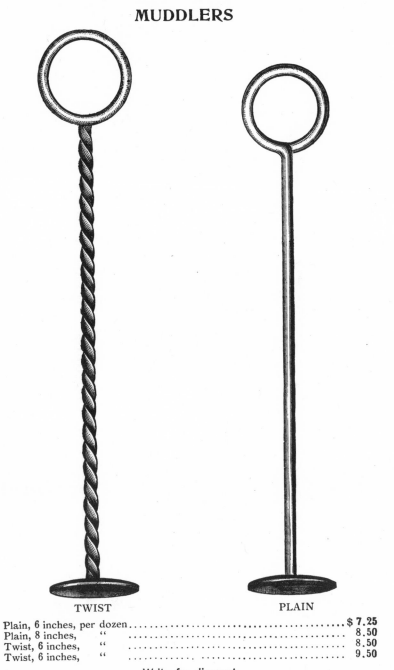

TWIST   PLAIN

Plain, 6 inches, per dozen..$ 7.25
Plain, 8 inches,   " 8.50
Twist, 6 inches,   " 8.50
Twist, 6 inches,   " 9.50

Write for discount.

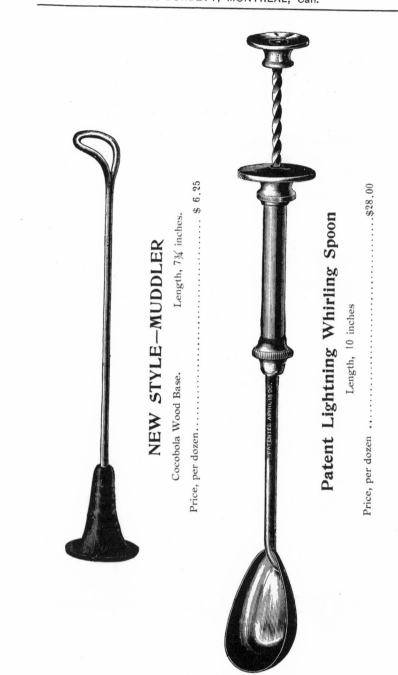

NEW STYLE—MUDDLER

Cocobola Wood Base.   Length, 7¾ inches.

Price, per dozen.................. $ 6.25

Patent Lightning Whirling Spoon

Length, 10 inches

Price, per dozen $28.00

Write for discount.

Walker's Quick and Easy Wedge Pointed, Tempered Ice Picks.

Anti-rust nickel plated.   Every one tested and guaranteed.

Brass wire springs in all Spring Picks.

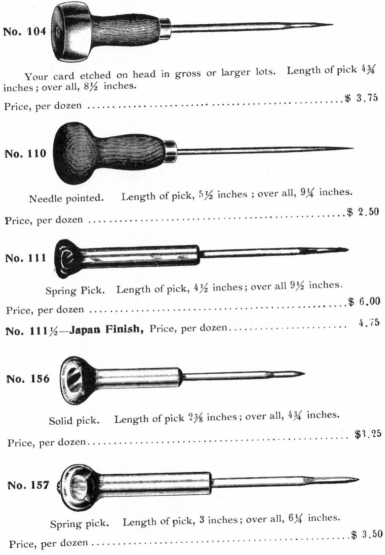

No. 104

Your card etched on head in gross or larger lots.   Length of pick 4¾ inches ; over all, 8½ inches.

Price, per dozen ....$ 3.75

No. 110

Needle pointed.   Length of pick, 5½ inches ; over all, 9¼ inches.

Price, per dozen ....$ 2.50

No. 111

Spring Pick.   Length of pick, 4½ inches; over all 9½ inches.

Price, per dozen ....$ 6.00

No. 111½—Japan Finish, Price, per dozen...................... 4.75

No. 156

Solid pick.   Length of pick 2⅜ inches ; over all, 4¾ inches.

Price, per dozen...$3.25

No. 157

Spring pick.   Length of pick, 3 inches; over all, 6¼ inches.

Price, per dozen ....$ 3.50

Write for discount.

ICE SHAVES

No. 0—Plain handle, cast steel blade, price, per dozen ....$ 2.50

No. 1—Polished handle, plain iron head, cast steel blade, price, per doz.$ 2.75
No. 100—Polished handle, nickel head and blade, cast steel blade,
      price, per dozen.................................... .... 4.00

No. 10—" Star " ice shave, head and blade full nickel plated, cast
      iron blade, price, per dozen..........................$ 2.75
      All the above packed 1 dozen in a box.

Restaurateurs' Ice Shaves

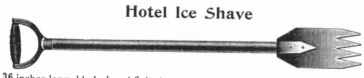

No. A—Black walnut handle, length 10 inch, hand forged, per dozen..$10.50
No. 2—   "   "   "   11 "   "   "   .. 11.50
No. 3—   "   "   "   18 "   "   "   .. 13.50
No. 4—   "   "   "   22 "   "   "   .. 15.50
No. 5—   "   "   "   26 "   "   "   .. 17.50

Hotel Ice Shave

36 inches long, blade 4 and 6 inches, made of high grade American
      steel, price, each....................................$ 2.15

Write for discount.

All Copper Stop Funnel

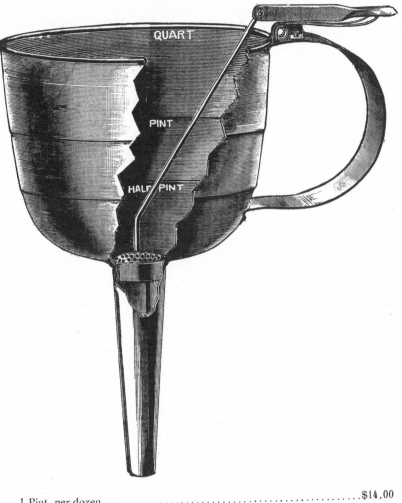

1 Pint, per dozen...$14.00
1 Quart, per dozen 17.00
2   "   " 26.25

This is a combined Funnel, Strainer and Measure.   Gauges from ½ pint to 1 quart. Just the thing for filling small bottles, as it prevents waste in overflowing, as the flow can be stopped instantly ; not liable to get out of order. Will enter the mouth of ½ pint bottles.

Write for discount.

MOVABLE STRAINER

Movable Strainer Funnel

This Funnel supplies an article long needed by bar and hotel keepers.

The above sectionel illustration is full size of No. 1 Funnel, and will easily show how readily the strainer can be taken out, cleansed and replaced, or a new one put in without the aid of a tinner.

PRICES :

4 in., for filling ½ pints, each . .$ 0.60
5 "   "   1   "   "   . . 0.70
6 "   "   1 quart "   . . 0.80
7 "   "   ½ gallon "   . . 1.00
8 "   "   1   "   "   . . 1.60

Liquor Measures

The Copper Measures here shown are six in number—namely, gill, half-pint, pint, quart, 2 quart, 1 gallon—made from New Haven copper, giving them a beautiful polish. The bottom is made to form a rim around, which protects the bottom from wearing out, and when properly sealed they become a durable standard of measure, and not liable to get out of order.

Copper Measures, per set of six.$ 6.00
  1 gallon, per dozen. 18.50
  ½   "   " 14.50
  1 quart,   " 12.00
  1 pint,   " 8.50
  ½   "   " 6.00
  1 gill,   " 5.50

We also keep in stock 2, 3 and 5 gallon Copper Measures.

Write for discount.

D 21—New Tin Funnel with Strainer

½ Pint, per dozen ....$ 7.25

1 Pint, per dozen 9.50

1 Quart, per dozen..................... 12.50

Automatic Funnel Jigger

This article has been produced by one who has had many years of experience in dispensing drinks, and he found a constant need for an article that would combined both all the uses of a Graduated Jigger, and Pousse Café and Float making contrivance.

Our little Combination Funnel Jigger is made of Britannia metal, and is quadruple silver plated. The Graduate is marked off on the inside, showing ½, 1, 1½ and 2 ounces.

It will make one dozen Pousse Cafés as easily as one. It is almost instantaneous in making a brandy, or other float. This dispenses with the old-time method of using a spoon in order to float a liquid.

It is compact and neat, and once used, becomes indispensable.

Price, each ....$ 4.50

Write for discount.

Climax Strainer
Nickel-Plated

Climax Strainer in position for use

Length, 3⅞ inches, per dozen.....................................$11.00

Cup Strainer
Silver-Plated

Depth, 3 inches, Top, 3¼ inches, per dozen. $26.00
Write for discount.

Ribbed Strainer

Silver-Plated

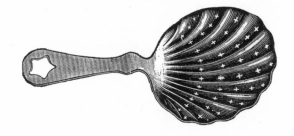

Length, 5½ inches, per dozen $6.25

Excelsior Strainer

Silver=Plated

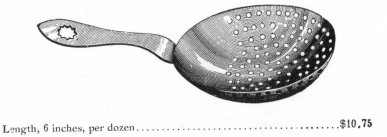

Length, 6 inches, per dozen....................................$10.75

Write for discount.

Absinthe Drip

Nickel-Plated

Height 2¾ inches.   Top 3¾ inches.

P. & H., per dozen $23.00
R.   per dozen 15.50

Dipper Strainer

Nickel-Plated

Length, 6½ inches, Depth, 1¾ inches, per dozen...................$23.00

Write for discount.

Heavy Copper Funnels

With Loose Strainers

No. 233, ¼ pint, per dozen ....$ 5.35
    234, ½ pint, per dozen 5.35
    235, 1 pint, per dozen 6.00
    236, 1 quart, per dozen...................................... 7.50
    237, 2 quart, per dozen...................................... 10.00
    238, 4 quart, per dozen...................................... 18.50

Extra Heavy Copper Funnels

Without Strainers

FULL MEASUREMENT

No. 239, ¼ pint, per dozen ....$ 6.00
    240, ½ pint, per dozen 6.00
    241, 1 pint, per dozen 6.75
    242, 1 quart, per dozen...................................... 8.00
    243, 2 quart, per dozen...................................... 11.25
    244, 4 quart, per dozen...................................... 18.50

Square Spouts, per dozen, extra, $2.00.

Write for discount.

All Copper Valve Funnels

This Funnel is a Combined Measure and Funnel

The best article of the kind on the market.   A trial will convince one of its merits.   The measure gauges from one-half pint to one quart.

No. 909, 1 pint, per dozen..$14.00
    910, 1 quart, per dozen.. 17.00
    912, 2 quart, per dozen.. 28.00

All Copper Ale and Beer Measures

GLASS INDICATOR

No. 332, 2 quart, each...$ 2.90
    333, 3 quart, each.. 3.40
    334, 4 quart, each.. 4.00

ALL COPPER, NICKEL-PLATED

No. 432, 2 quart, each.. 3.60
    433, 3 quart, each.. 4.00
    434, 4 quart, each.. 4.40

Write for discount.

Copper Liquor Measures

Made of heavy copper, with capacity gauge, heavy wire handle.

No. 92, 2 gallon, each **$6.00**
    93, 3 gallon, each **6.75**
    94, 4 gallon, each **7.25**
    95, 5 gallon, each **8.50**

Combination Measure and Funnel

Made from heavy copper, tinned on inside. Very useful, convenient for filling bottles and jugs, no extra funnel required.

No. 251, 1 pint,   per dozen **$10.50**
    252, 1 quart, per dozen **14.50**
    253, 2 quart, per dozen **19.00**
    254, 4 quart, per dozen **25.75**

Write for discount.

Barrel Funnel

Made of heavy copper, has fine perforated removable strainer.

1 gallon, each...$ 2.70
2 gallon, each... 3.00
3 gallon, each... 3.40
4 gallon, each... 3.70
5 gallon, each... 4.00

All Copper Measures

These Measures are made of heavy copper and are absolutely perfect.

No. 82, 2 gallon, each.......................................$ 6.00
83, 3 gallon, each 6.75
84, 4 gallon, each....................................... 7.25
85, 5 gallon, each....................................... 8.50

Write for discount.

Bar Strainer

Per dozen $15.50

Julep Strainer—Lindley

Per dozen $15.50

Write for discount. 4

Regular Jigger
Nickel-Plated

Per dozen....................$ 8.50

Per dozen, silver-plated, net, ex.   3.25

Combination Jigger
Nickel-Plated

Per dozen ....$ 9.25

Per dozen, silver-plated, net, ex.   4.50

Pony Jigger
Nickel-Plated

Per dozen $7.75

Per dozen, silver-plated, net, ex. 3.25

Sugar Box
Nickel-Plated

Per dozen $31.00

Per dozen, silver-plated, net, ex. 4.50

Write for discount.

Hard Rubber Shaker

D85—An absolutely perfect shaker. The cleanest and most practical article ever offered to the trade. Acide do not effect it.

Price, per dozen $34.00

Spun Shaker

	HEIGHT	Diameter BOTTOM	TOP	PER DOZ.
Cocktail	3 5/8 in.	2 in.	2 7/8 in.	$12.25
Small	5 "	2 1/4 "	3 1/4 "	13.00
Medium	1 5/8 "	2 1/2 "	3 3/8 "	14.00
D..............	5 1/4 "	2 1/4 "	3 5/8 "	14.00
C..............	5 3/4 "	2 1/4 "	3 7/8 "	15.50
Large..........	5 3/4 "	2 5/8 "	3 3/4 "	17.00
7 inch. D........	7 "	2 1/4 "	3 7/8 "	20.00

Write for discount.

Lemonade Shaker

All Copper

No. 727, 4   in. high, 2¾ in. at top, per dozen ....$ 6.25
    728, 5¼ in. high, 3¼ in. at top,   " 7.00
    729, 6   in. high, 3¾ in. at top,   " 7.75
    730, 7   in. high, 4   in. at top,   " 8.25

All Copper, Nickel-Plated

No. 827, 5   in. high, 2¾ in. at top, per dozen ....$ 7.00
    828, 5¼ in. high, 3¼ in. at top   " 8.25
    829, 6   in. high, 3¾ in. at top,   " 9.00
    830, 7   in. high, 4   in. at top,   " 11.25

Aluminum

5   in. high, per dozen.. 6.25
5½ in. high,   " 7.00
6   in. high,   " 7.75

Seamless Spun Shakers

Silver-Lined inside.   Nickel outside

No. 831, 3¾ in. high, 2¾ in. at top, per dozen ....$ 8.25
    832, 5¼ in. high, 3¼ in. at top,   " 12.00
    833, 6   in. high, 3¾ in. at top,   " 12.50
    834, 7   in. high, 4   in. at top,   " 19.50

Write for discount.

Shaker with Strainer

Silver lined, Strainer attached to Shaker.

No. 843, 6 in. high, 3¾ in. at top, per dozen $20.00

Combination Shakers

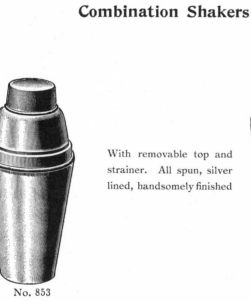

With removable top and strainer. All spun, silver lined, handsomely finished

No. 853

No. 223

No. 853, 8 in. high, per dozen..................................... $21.25
No. 223, 1¼ pints, nickel plated, per dozen......................... 26.75
No. 233, 1½ "   "   "   " 33.00

Write for discount.

No. 1530—Aluminum Combination Shakers

No. 1531—Aluminum Combination Shakers

Size, 7½ inches high

Price, per dozen $14.00

Size, 8 inches high

Price, per dozen $16.25

No. 1552—Aluminum Lemon Juice Extractor

Price, per dozen..$ 2.40

Write for discount.

No. 1540—Aluminum Sugar Shakers

Polished or sat'n fin'shed. Size, 4 inches high
Price, per dozen..................$ 7.75

No. 1512—Alum=inum Salt and Pepper Shakers

Satin finished, with burn-ished lines.
Size, 4¾ inches high, 2⅛ inches diameter.
Price, per dozen....$ 5.90

No. 1513—Aluminum Salt and Pepper Shakers

Satin finished and polished.
Size 2½ inches high, 1¼ inches diameter.
Price, per dozen.........$ 2.00

Write for discount.

No. 1510—Aluminum Salt and Pepper Shakers

Satin finished, with knurls and burnished lines.
Size, 2¾ inches high, 2 inches diameter.
Price, per dozen.........$ 3.10

Brass Liquor Cocks

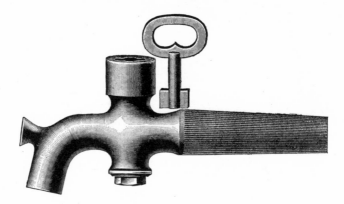

Nut and Washer.   Loose Key.   To Drive.

No.			Per doz.
630 X.	⅜	inch	$ 8.00
631 X.	½	"	10.50
632 X.	⅝	"	14.25
633 X.	¾	"	17.50

Nut and Washer.   Loose Key.   To Screw.

No.			Per doz.
640X.	⅜	inch	$ 8.40
641X.	½	"	11.25
642X.	⅝	"	15.50
643X.	¾	"	19.00

Guaranteed for 150 lbs. pressure.

Write for discount.

Brass Bottling Cocks

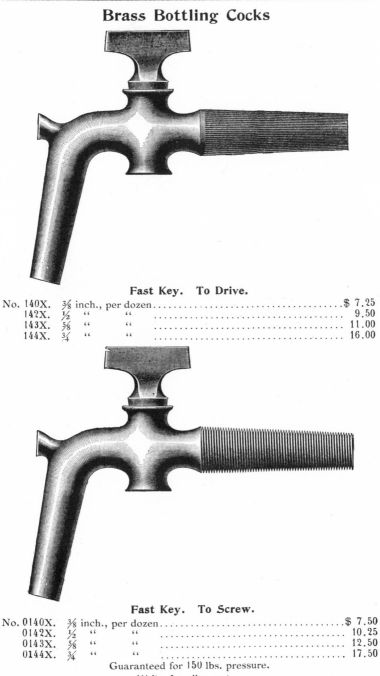

Fast Key. To Drive.

No. 140X.   ⅜ inch., per dozen....................................$ 7.25
    142X.   ½   "   " 9.50
    143X.   ⅝   "   " 11.00
    144X.   ¾   "   " 16.00

Fast Key. To Screw.

No. 0140X.   ⅜ inch., per dozen....................................$ 7.50
    0142X.   ½   "   " 10.25
    0143X.   ⅝   "   " 12.50
    0144X.   ¾   "   " 17.50

Guaranteed for 150 lbs. pressure.

Write for discount.

McKenna's Home Bottler

THE OLD WAY

With our BOTTLING FAUCET beer can be bottled perfectly by any person without the possibility of spilling a drop or losing any of the natural gas or spirit of the beer, as the spigot inserted in the neck of the bottle serves as a cork until the bottle is completely filled with solid beer, all the foam returning to the keg, as shown in the illustration. No air vent is required in the keg, as the air and foam from the bottle returning to the keg keep an ample pressure.

Under the old style of bottling the air vent necessary to allow the beer to flow permits the gas to escape from the beer, thus causing it to become flat before it is consigned to the bottle.

McKenna's Home Bottler

THE NEW WAY

With our BOTTLER the beer in the bottle is just as fresh as before the keg was tapped.

No matter how warm the beer may be when the keg is tapped, each bottle can be completely filled with solid beer without the possibility of any foam slopping over.

The faucet is made specially for family use, and only one trial is necessary to convince any one of its superiority over the old method.

Price, each . . . . $ 3.00

Write for discount.

Brass Racking Cocks

Loose Key. To Screw.

No. 39X.	¼ inch., per dozen	....	$ 5.50
No. 40X.	⅜ " "	....	7 25
No. 41X.	½ " "	....	10 25
No. 42X.	⅝ " "	....	14 50
No. 43X.	¾ " "	....	17 50
No. 45X.	1 " "	....	30 00

Loose Key. To Drive.

No. 29X.	¼ inch., per dozen	....	$ 5.25
No. 30X.	⅜ " "	....	7.00
No. 31X.	½ " "	....	9.50
No. 32X.	⅝ " "	....	13.00
No. 33X.	¾ " "	....	16.00
No. 35X.	1 " "	....	28.25

Guaranteed for 150 lbs. Pressure.

Write for discount.

Plain Bibbs

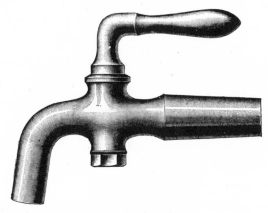

For Lead Pipe No. 7

Sizes	¼	⅜	½	⅝	¾	1
Rough, per dozen	$7.25	$8.75	$11.00	$13.00	$16.50	$25.50
Finished, "	8.00	9.50	12.00	14.50	19.00	28.50
Nickel plated, "	9.50	11.00	14.00	16.00	21.00	31.00

Compression Plain Bibbs

For Lead Pipe No. 1

Size, inch	⅜	½	⅝	¾	1
Rough, per dozen	$7.50	$8.40	$9.50	$13.50	$24.00
Finished, "	8.00	8.75	10.25	14.40	27.00
Nickel plated, "	9.50	10.25	12.00	16.00	29.50

Guaranteed for 150 lbs. Pressure.

Write for discount.

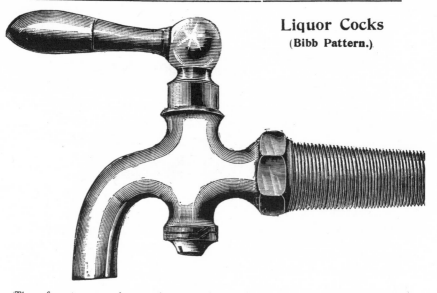

Liquor Cocks
(Bibb Pattern.)

These faucets are made extra heavy, and we guarantee them to be absolutely perfect in every respect.

⅜ inch opening... $1.50   ⅝ inch opening... $2.50   1 inch opening... $4.50
½ "   "   ... 2.00   ¾ "   "   ... 3.00   1¼ "   "   ... 7.00

Bottling Cocks

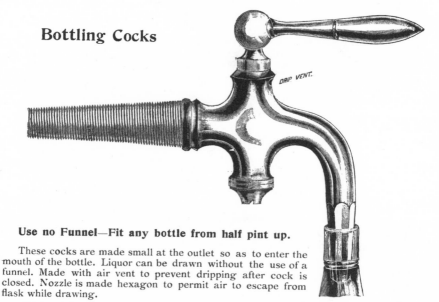

DRIP VENT.

Use no Funnel—Fit any bottle from half pint up.

These cocks are made small at the outlet so as to enter the mouth of the bottle. Liquor can be drawn without the use of a funnel. Made with air vent to prevent dripping after cock is closed. Nozzle is made hexagon to permit air to escape from flask while drawing.

Price, each $2.60

Write for discount.

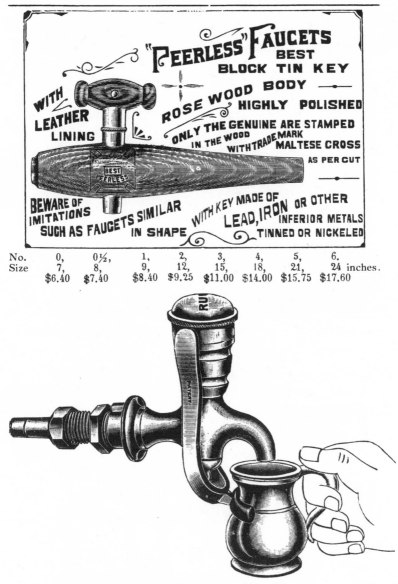

No.	0,	0½,	1,	2,	3,	4,	5,	6.	
Size	7,	8,	9,	12,	15,	18,	21,	24 inches.	
	$6.40	$7.40	$8.40	$9.25	$11.00	$14.00	$15.75	$17.60	

The Rapid Self=closing Tap

For quick serving or bottling of Ale, Wines, Spirits, Hot and Cold Water and other Liquids.

The act of placing the Measure, Glass, Jug, Bottle or other receptacle under the spout of the Tap TURNS IT ON.

The Tap turns itself off when the vessel used is removed.   The action is instantaneous.

The most effective and useful Tap yet invented for simplicity and efficiency.

Write for discount.

Write for discount.

No. 1592. Pitcher—Pint
Plain......................$6.25   With Ice Guard......$7.25

No. 1591. Pitcher—Quart
With Ice Guard............$8.00
Quality Guaranteed,

No. 1131—Bar Pitcher with Guard

White Metal

Price, each. $8.00

Ice Water Pitchers

All Copper, Nickel-Plated

Spun from heavy copper ; body double seamed to bottom ; very heavy silver plated on pure block tin lining ; spout has lip to prevent ice from flowing out

No. 1, 1 pint, per dozen. $41.00
"   2, 2 pint, per dozen. 44.00
"   3, 3 pint, per dozen. 48.50
"   4, 4 pint, per dozen. 56.00
"   121, 1 pint, White Metal, Nickel Plated, each. 3.25
"   122, 1½ pint, White Metal, Nickel Plated, each. 3.75

Write for discount.   5

Sausage Cooker
Planished IXX Tin

Made from IXX Melyn tin, with perforated tray and copper bottom. This Cooker steams the sausage and is a great improvement over the old method of boiling them in water. Nothing better.

No. 916, planished tin. Each $5.50
917, planished tin, nickel-plated. Each 6.25

Size, 12 in. diameter; 12 in. high.

Ice Water Pail

Ice Water Pails for hotels, for carrying ice water to guests' rooms ; made of heavy copper, highly finished and strongly made.

No. 1, 1 gallon, per dozen..$35.25
2, 2 gallon, per dozen.. 53.00

Write for discount.

Bottle Tray

Made from Heavy Brass, Nickel or Silver-Plated if Desired

No. 3, polished brass, per dozen ....$ 3.25
4, nickel-plated, per dozen..................................... 4.50
5, silver-plated, per dozen 10.50

Size, 3⅝ in. diameter, inside.

Brass Tray for Individual Glass

Made from Heavy Brass, Highly Finished

No. 1, 4⅛ in. diameter, per dozen.................................. $3.25
No. 2, 3⅝ in. diameter, per dozen................................. 3.00

Iroquois Bar Pitcher

Made from one piece of heavy copper, nickel-plated outside, silver-plated inside.

Price, per dozen...$44.00

Height, 4⅝ in. ; diameter, 4¼ in.

Write for discount.

Heavy Nickel=Plated Spice Tray

No. 1014, base 5 in. diameter, height 6 in.,   per dozen . . . . $46.25.
1015, base 8 in. diameter, height 4⅝ in.   "   . . . . 41.25.

Gem Bar Spice Stand
Heavy Nickel-Plated

4¾ inches high.   Base 7⅝ inches diameter.

Per dozen $60.00

Write for discount.

Delft Cracker and Cheese Bowls

Dark Blue Mottled Bowl with nickel-plated rim and cover.   Partition in center.

No. 5, 8½ in. diameter outside at top. Each...................... $4.50
6, 11½ in. diameter outside at top. Each...................... 7.50

Cracker and Cheese Bowls

China Bowl with nickel-plated rim and cover.   Partition in center.

No. 3, 8 in. diameter outside at top. Each....................... $3.75
4, 11 in. diameter outside at top. Each....................... 6.50

Write for discount.

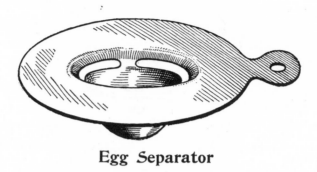

Egg Separator

Very handy for separating the yoke from the white of an egg. Can be used for household kitchen purposes or for Bar Rooms, being the only standard article for making up Gold and Silver Fiz.

Price, Aluminum, each... 35 cts.
Price, Pressed Tin, each .... 30 cts.

Sausage Cookers

The Cooker steams the sausage and is a great improvement over the old method of boiling them in water. It is far superior to any article ever invented for this use.

No. 905, copper, each...$11.00
   915, nickel-plated, each 12.50

Size, 12 in. diameter ; 10 in. high.

Write for discount.

The Safety Pan and Plate Lifter
Patent applied for

Nickel plated throughout. For lifting stew pans, etc., from the top of the stove and taking pies, cakes, etc., from the oven. A weight on the prongs of the malleable casting causes the casting to grip wires firmly, thereby preventing shipping.

One dozen in box. Weight per gross 80 pounds ; net 68 pounds. Dimension per gross 42 x 30 x 20.

Price, per dozen .... $ 3.75

Nut Crackers

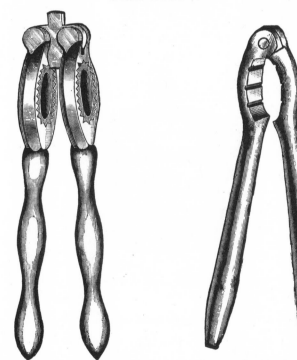

No. 1.   Nickel plated malleable iron.   No. 2.   Nickel plated grey iron

Per dozen....................$4.25   Per dozen....................$1.75

Write for discount.

Foot Rail Bracket

2 inch, 2¼ inch, 2½ inch, 2¾ in.

Polished brass, each $3.75

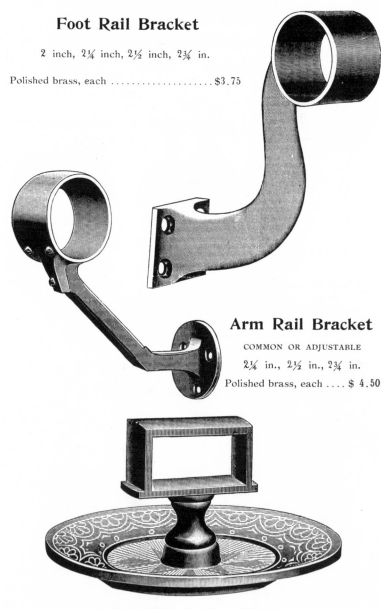

Arm Rail Bracket

COMMON OR ADJUSTABLE

2¼ in., 2½ in., 2¾ in.

Polished brass, each .... $ 4.50

Safety Match Box Holder

Black enamel finish, per dozen .... $ 1.50

Packed 1 dozen each in a paper box.

Write for discount.

MATCH STAND

For Safety Matches

Made from heavy brass, 4 in. diameter, 4 in. high ; weight, 13 oz.

No. 1, polished brass, per dozen................................. ... .$ 11.00

2, nickel-plated, per dozen 12.75

Match Stand and Ash Tray

For Safety Matches

Made from heavy brass ; 5 in. diameter and 3½ in. high ; weight, 12 oz.

No. 3, polished brass, lacquered, per dozen .... $ 12.75

4, nickel-plated, per dozen.................................... 14.00

5, brass, per dozen 3.50

6, nickel-plated, per dozen................................... 5.00

Write for discount.

Plain Heavy Hotel Trays

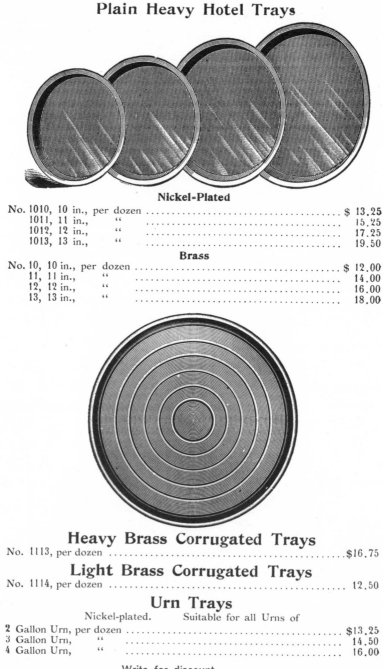

Nickel-Plated

No. 1010, 10 in., per dozen	....	$ 13.25
1011, 11 in., "	....	15.25
1012, 12 in., "	....	17.25
1013, 13 in., "	....	19.50

Brass

No. 10, 10 in., per dozen	....	$ 12.00
11, 11 in., "	....	14.00
12, 12 in., "	....	16.00
13, 13 in., "	....	18.00

Heavy Brass Corrugated Trays

No. 1113, per dozen $16.75

Light Brass Corrugated Trays

No. 1114, per dozen 12.50

Urn Trays

Nickel-plated.   Suitable for all Urns of

2 Gallon Urn, per dozen	....	$13.25
3 Gallon Urn, "	....	14.50
4 Gallon Urn, "	....	16.00

Write for discount.

No. 418—Aluminum Round Server

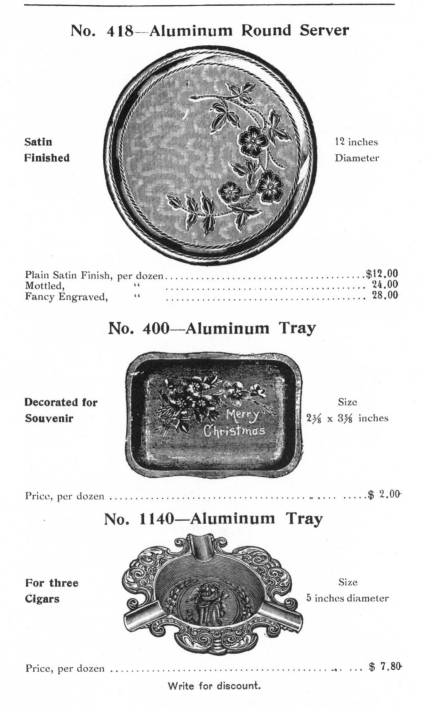

**Satin
Finished**

12 inches
Diameter

Plain Satin Finish, per dozen......................................$12.00
Mottled,   " 24.00
Fancy Engraved,   " 28.00

No. 400—Aluminum Tray

**Decorated for
Souvenir**

Size
2⅜ x 3⅝ inches

Price, per dozen ....$ 2.00

No. 1140—Aluminum Tray

**For three
Cigars**

Size
5 inches diameter

Price, per dozen ....,. ... $ 7.80

Write for discount.

Rubber Pitcher Mats

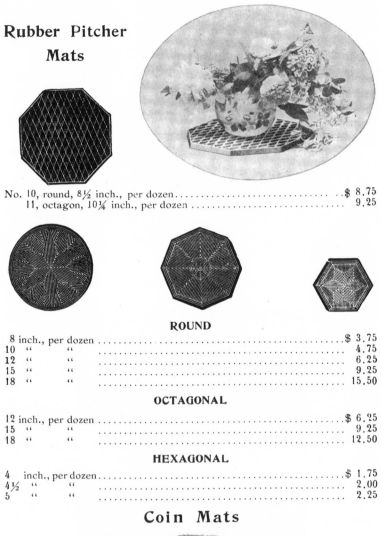

No. 10, round, 8½ inch., per dozen.............................$ 8.75
11, octagon, 10¼ inch., per dozen 9.25

ROUND

8 inch., per dozen		$ 3.75
10 " "		4.75
12 " "		6.25
15 " "		9.25
18 " "		15.50

OCTAGONAL

12 inch., per dozen		$ 6.25
15 " "		9.25
18 " "		12.50

HEXAGONAL

4 inch., per dozen		$ 1.75
4½ " "		2.00
5 " "		2.25

Coin Mats

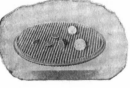

Oblong, 6 x 9 inch., per dozen.....................................$13.50
Round, 8 " " 13.50
" 10 " " 17.60

Write for discount.

Cuspidore Mat

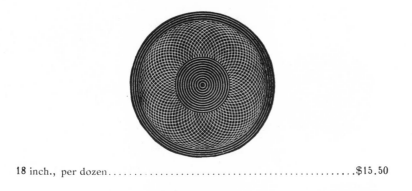

18 inch., per dozen..$15.50

Perforated Mats

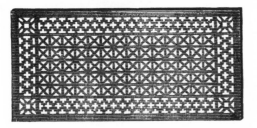

H.

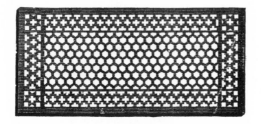

I.

¼ inch. thick, per square foot.....................................$ 1.00
⅜ "   "   "   " 1.40
½ "   "   "   .   " 1.75

Write for discount.

CUSPIDORE

Nos. 23 or 26 — Heavy Vase Pattern

No. 23, 9½ x 6½ inch., Brass, per dozen ....$ 37.00
23, "   "   "   Nickel   " 38.75
26, 12 x 8½ "   Brass   " 54.25
26 "   "   "   Nickel   " 55.80

No. 34 With Rubber Feet

No. 34, 9½ x 9 inch., Brass, per dozen.............................$55.80
34, "   "   "   Nickel,   " 57.35
Write for discount.

Cuspidores and Spittoons

Nos. 14 or 20

No. 14, 8½ x 5½ inch., Brass, per dozen..........................$31.00
14, " " " Nickel " 32.50
20, 11½ x 6 " Brass " 55.80
20, " " " Nickel " 60.50

Bronze Spittoon

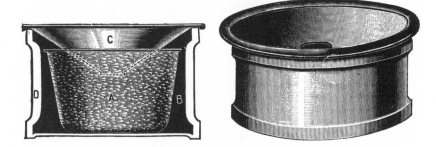

Lined with Heavy Cast Steel and supplied with Agate Iron Cup

A.—Cup   C.—Removable Top.
B.—Steel Lining.   D.—Bronze body.

No. 28, Bronze, 8 x 4 inch., per dozen $49.60

Write for discount.

Cuspidores and Spittoons

No. 16.—Hotel Pattern

No. 16, 10 x 6 inch., Brass, per dozen...............................$65.00

16, 10 x 6 inch., Nickel   " 66.50

Nos. 17 or 18—With Rubber Feet

No. 17, 7½ x 5½ inch., Brass, per dozen $32.50

17, "   "   "   Nickel,   " 34.00

18, 8½ x 6½ "   Brass,   " 40.50

18, "   "   "   Nickel,   " 42.00

Write for discount.

Nos. 10 or 12—Spittoons and Cuspidores

No. 10, 7½ x 3 inch., Brass, per dozen................. ....$21.75
10, " " " Nickel, " 23.50
12, 8½ x 3 inch., Brass, " 26.50
12, " " " Nickel, " 28.00

No. 15—Railroad Car Pattern

No. 15, 7 x 4 inch., Brass, per dozen...............................$29.50
15, " " " Nickel, " 31.00

Nos. 24 or 25—Heavy Bronze Spittoons

No. 24, 8 x 4 inch., per dozen $37.50
25, 10 x 4 " " 51.00

Write for discount.   6

Nos. 1, 2 or 3—Loaded, Self=Righting Spittoons

No. 1, Polished Brass, 6½ x 4¾ inch., per dozen $17.00
1, Nickel Plated,   "   "   "   " 18.50
2, Polished Brass, 7½ x 5¾ "   " 18.50
2, Nickel Plated,   "   "   "   " 20.00
3, Polished Brass, 8½ x 6½ "   " 28.00
3, Nickel Plated,   "   "   "   " 29.50

Nos. 7, 8 or 9—Unloaded Spittoons

No. 7, Polished Brass, 6¼ x 4¾ inch., per dozen $14.00
7, Nickel Plated,   "   "   "   " 15.50
8, Polished Brass, 7½ x 5¾ "   " 15.50
8, Nickel Plated,   "   "   "   " 17.00
9, Polished Brass, 8½ x 6½ "   " 25.00
9, Nickel Plated,   "   "   "   " 26.50

Write for discount.

THE CROWN

No. 202, all Brass Cuspidores, per dozen...........................$17.75
212,   "   "   Nickel-Plated, per dozen................ 19.25

THE PALACE

No. 201, all Brass Cuspidores, per dozen $15.50
211,   "   "   Nickel-Plated, per dozen................ 17.00

Write for discount.

CUSPIDORES

Size, 9¼ in. diameter ; 9 in. high ; weighs about 6 lbs.   Heavy
weighted bottom, finely finished.

No. 1228, all Brass, per dozen....................................$53.00
1229, Nickel-Plated, per dozen 60.00

Size, 7½ in. diameter ; 4¾ in. high.

No. 1200, Polished Brass, per dozen $28.00
1201, Nickel-Plated,   " 33.00

Write for discount.

Sanitary Cuspidores

These Cuspidores have vitrified stone reservoirs (mottled blue) with heavy spun brass tops, removable, which makes them easily cleaned, and are adapted for hotels, restaurants or public buildings.

No. 1230, Brass, per dozen......................................$17.00

1230½, Nickel-plated, per dozen........................... 20.00

230, Brass, per dozen.. 14.00

230½, Nickel-plated, per dozen........................... 17.00

Large size, 10 in. diameter ; 4 in. high.
Small size, 8 in. diameter ; 4 in. high.

Brass Cuspidore—Grand

Size, 9 in. diameter ; 7¼ in. high. Very heavy weighted bottom, self-righting, beautifully finished.

No. 1222, All brass, per dozen $31.25

1223, Nickel-plated, per dozen 34.00

Write for discount.

Niagara Cuspidore

No. 1231, All Brass, per dozen $28.00
1232, Nickel-plated, per dozen................................. 31.00

Size, 8 inch. diameter ; 6 inch. high.

No. 63—Cuspidore

Price, All Brass, per dozen $51.50

Oval Bottoms

No. 101, per dozen........................... ....$12.50

Write for discount.

The Royal

Extra Large Size

No. 1203, All Brass Cuspidores, per dozen $21.50

1213, All Brass Cuspidores, per dozen, nickel-plated............. 28.00

New Self-Righting Cuspidore

No. 1214, All Brass, per dozen $15.50

1215, Nickel-plated, per dozen............................... 17.00

Write for discount.

No. 30—"Non=Spillable" Cuspidore

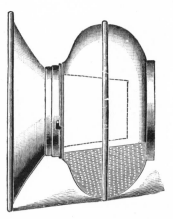

No. 30, 8½ x 6½ in., Brass, per dozen............................$39.00

30, "   "   Nickel, " 40.00

Write for discount.

Brass Cuspidore—Imperial

Size, 9 in. diameter ; 11 in. high ; weighs 8 lbs.

Very heavy weighted bottom, self-righting, beautifully finished, nothing in the market so elaborate.

No. 1216, All Brass, per dozen.....................................$54.00

1217, Nickel-plated, per dozen............... .... 59.00

Giant

Small size, 8¾ in. diameter ; 3¾ in. high.
Large size, 10¼ in. diameter ; 4 in. high.

These Cuspidores are for hotels, saloons, club houses or public buildings ; will not jam or break ; large size weighs 10 lbs. ; small size weighs 6 lbs.

Heavy Brass Cuspidore, solid iron lined, with heavy loose cover ; two sizes.

No. 888, All Brass, per dozen......................................$39.00

889, Nickel-plated, per dozen.................................. 44.50

1218, Brass, per dozen... 41.75

1219, Nickel-plated, per dozen........ .... 47.25

Write for discount.

Brass Cuspidore—Eclipse

Size, 9 in. diameter ; 12 in. high ; weight about 8 lbs. Very heavy weighted bottom, self-righting, finished beautifully.

No. 1220, All Brass, per dozen.....................................$54.00
1221, Nickel-plated, per dozen... 59.00
220, aluminoid—a handsome Cuspidore ; made of metal with a
finish equal to Nickel, per dozen......................... 39.00

Brass Cuspidore—Bon=Ton

Size 11 in. diameter ; 6¼ in. high ; weight, 5 lbs.

Heavily weighted bottom, self-righting, finely finished. Suitable for halls, hotels or club rooms.

No. 1226, All Brass, per dozen......................................$39.00
1227, Nickel-plated, per dozen................................. 44.50

Write for discount.

Montreal Cuspidore

Very heavy, finely finished ; suitable for halls, hotels and club rooms.

Size, 10 in. wide ; 5 in. high ; weight 11 lbs.

No. 10, Cuspidore, all Nickel-plated, per dozen $36.00
    "   "   Nickel-plated Top and Aluminum finished base, per doz. 30.00

No. 1190, 1191—Cigar Cutters

Nos. 1190 or 1191 Cigar Cutters with advertisement stamped on some in plain bloc letters (not to exceed 40).

Price, Steel Nickel-plated, per 100.................................$42.00
    "   "   "   " 1000...................................186.00
    "   " per 100... 37.00
    "   " " 1000...151.00

Write for discount.

Ribbed Towel Holder

Small, 3 inches, per gross.........................$22.00

Large, 4⅛ inches, per gross............ .... 26.00

Hold Fast Towel Holder

Finely Nickel Plated

Towel easily and securely adjusted.

Per dozen...................................$3.50

Champagne Tap Cutter

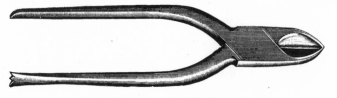

No. 13½   Length 6¾ inches.

Per dozen $18.50

Write for discount.

Silvered Bottle Tubes   ## Patent Self-Closing Essence Tube

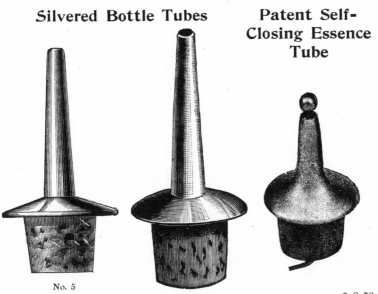

No. 5

Short, per gross .... $ 8.50
Long, per gross 9.75
Above with Valve, per gross, extra, $ 0.75
Patent Self-Closing Essence Tube, per dozen........................ $ 4.00
No. 5 Nickel-Plated Tube, per dozen................................ 2.25

Wire Towel Holders

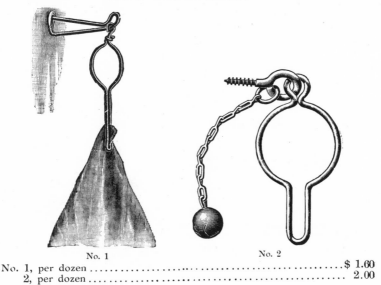

No. 1   No. 2

No. 1, per dozen .... $ 1.60
2, per dozen 2.00

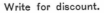
Write for discount.

Club Soda Bottle Holder

No. 1, Nickel-plated, per dozen.....................................$15.75
    2, Silver-plated, per dozen 22.00

Ginger Ale Bottle Holder

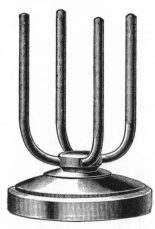

No. 3, per dozen..$9.25
Nickel-plated, height, 4½ inches.

Write for discount.

Rubber Stopper

No. 1, per hundred...$10.00

2, "   " 5.00

Perfection Bottle Stopper

Absolutely Air Tight. Perfect Freshness retained in all Bottled Goods.

Fits Large Neck Quarts.

They are especially useful where you have to keep opened bottles of ginger ale, seltzer, mineral water and even champagne. By keeping these bottles closed with the perfection stoppers the gas is kept from escaping and the liquid just as fresh as when the bottle was opened. In this way you can use the entire bottle to the very last drop and not have to throw away half of it on account of the contents becoming stale, as when you use any other kind of stopper. Will fit any size bottle. Made of best rubber with nickel-plated top and patent self-closing spring.

Price, per dozen..$ 4.50

Write for discount.

No. 5 — Junior Globe Electric Cigar Lighter and Cutter

This style is especially adapted for use in places where they do not care to attach to ceiling. It hangs from a **nickel arm and base,** which consists of an

AUTOMATIC CIGAR CUTTER

This is operated by **two wet batteries.**

Price, complete................$20.00

No. 5—With Cutter

No. D 24
Cork Extractor

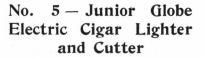

Wood handle. For pulling out corks which have fallen into bottle.

Price, each ......$ 0.35

Write for discount.

The Globe Electric Cigar Lighter

It is the most practical as well as most novel device of the kind ever offered. It is always ready, night or day. Why furnish your whole neighborhood with matches when 50 cents worth of gasoline will supply the wants of your trade for a year? The illustration represents the lighter in use. When the hand is withdrawn it closes automatically and extinguishes the flame. It lights when opened, the two points coming together and separating connect and break the electric circuit, making a spark which lights the wick. All points of wear are case hardened steel. The wick is of asbestos and therefore needs no trimming, lowering or raising. Two ounces of gasoline will last ten days. The Globe Lighter complete, consisting of one lighter, 24 feet of lamp wire attached, two electric batteries, one 4½ lb. spark coil, salamoniac, and full directions for putting up and charging batteries.

Price, complete $12.25

Full and explicit directions accompany each lighter, so that anyone can set it in successful operation ; no electrician necessary.

Hazard Cup

Wood, each ....$ 6.00
Leather, each.................................... 6.25
Wired, each 8.00

Write for discount.   7

No. 3501—Poker Dice

Made of imitation ivory. Will not break or corners wear off. Engraved with playing card faces—Ace, King, Queen, Jack, Ten and Nine. Size, ¾ inches, full regulation.

Price, per set of 5 ....$ 1.25

"   " dozen sets 14.00

No. D 283—Edgar Nutmeg Grater

A handy device which does the work effectually without grating the fingers.

Price, each ....$ 0.35

Pepper Shaker   Nutmeg Shaker

Pepper Shaker, per dozen.......................................$12.50

Nutmeg Shaker,   " 12.50

All Silver-plated, extra, per dozen 5.50

Write for discount.

Cracker and Cheese Bowl

Made from heavy stock.   Silver lined inside.   Nickel outside.
The above Bowl is made with partitions for both crackers and cheese.
No. 1, 12 in. high, 9 in. diameter.   Price each.......................$ 8.75

Nickel-plated

Made from heavy stock.   Silver lined inside.   Nickel outside.
The above Bowl is made with partitions for both crackers and cheese.
No. 2, 7 in. high, 10 in. diameter.   Each...........................$10.25

Write for discount.

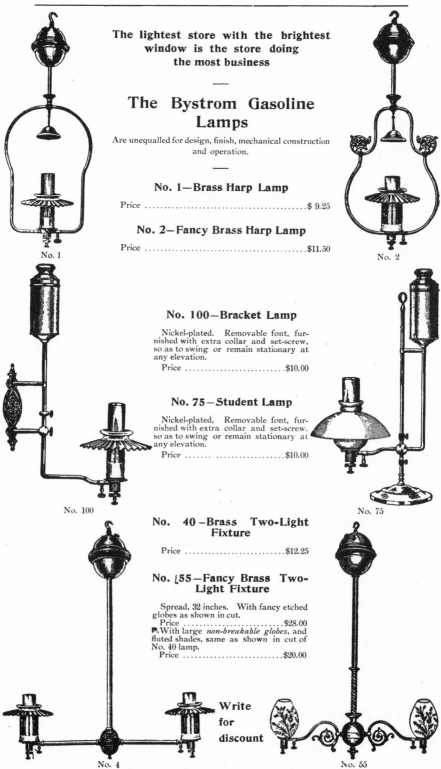

The lightest store with the brightest window is the store doing the most business

The Bystrom Gasoline Lamps

Are unequalled for design, finish, mechanical construction and operation.

No. 1—Brass Harp Lamp

Price ....$ 9.25

No. 2—Fancy Brass Harp Lamp

Price $11.50

No. 1

No. 2

No. 100—Bracket Lamp

Nickel-plated. Removable font, furnished with extra collar and set-screw, so as to swing or remain stationary at any elevation.
Price $10.00

No. 75—Student Lamp

Nickel-plated. Removable font, furnished with extra collar and set-screw, so as to swing or remain stationary at any elevation.
Price $10.00

No. 100

No. 75

No. 40—Brass Two-Light Fixture

Price $12.25

No. 55—Fancy Brass Two-Light Fixture

Spread, 32 inches. With fancy etched globes as shown in cut.
Price $28.00
With large *non-breakable globes*, and fluted shades, same as shown in cut of No. 40 lamp.
Price $20.00

Write
for
discount

No. 4

No. 55

The Bystrom Arc Lamp

The only successful Under-Generator Pressure Lamp on the market.

SAFE !   RELIABLE !

ECONOMICAL !

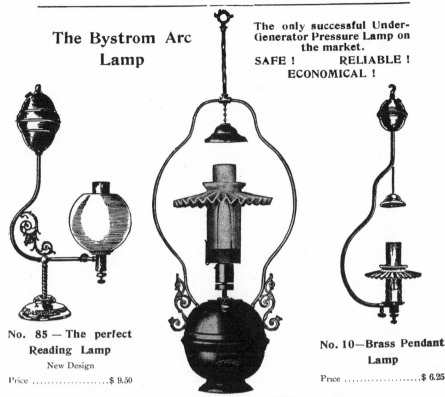

No. 85 — The perfect Reading Lamp

New Design

Price .... $ 9.50

No. 10—Brass Pendant Lamp

Price .... $ 6.25

Design No. 5.   Price..... $17.00

Surpasses all recently invented lights in power and is invaluable for all places where a large volume of light is desired at a small cost.

A Brilliant 750 Candle-Power Light at an Expense of 1-3 cent per hour.

or at one-fourth the cost of kerosene of the same candle-power. Two quarts of gasolene and sufficient air burns twelve hours.

The care and attention required is not more than necessary to keep a kerosene lamp in order. The lamp needs to be filled and air pumped in with foot pump furnished with each lamp. Time required, not more than 5 minutes per day.   No complicated construction. Anyone can operate the Lamp.   Must be seen in operation to be appreciated.

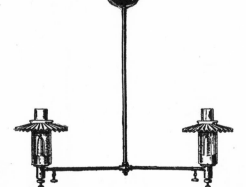

No. 30—Two-Light Fixture

Oxidized Copper Finish.

Price $11.50

Write for discount

The lightest store with the brightest window is the store doing the most business.

The Bystrom Gasoline Lamps

WITH THE

IMPROVED BYSTROM BURNER

The most complete line on the market.

For use in **Homes, Stores, Churches, Halls, Factories,** and all places where a superior light is required at a small cost.
Gives three times the light at one-fifth the cost of a kerosene lamp.

Permitted by the National Board of Fire Insurance Underwriters.

No. 20—Pendant Lamp
Oxidized Copper Finish
Price ....$ 6.25

Automatic 6 feet Spring Extension
Ornemental Brass.
Should be used on all hanging lamps. A great convenience.   Saves time. Saves mantles.
    Price ....$ 3.00

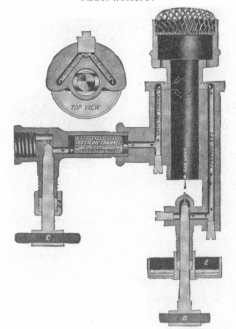

SECTIONAL VIEW

A—Wire Gauze.   AA—Inside Wire Gauze.   B—Needle Valve.   C—Cut-off.   BB—Cut-off Packing Nut.   E—Generating Cup.

The Bystrom Burner

is constructed on correct principles, and is one on which you can rely. We are furnishing a great many to equip fixtures of other manufacturers where their burners have proven worthless. We **are** the only manufacturers who are willing to do this and guarantee them to give satisfaction. **It works,** and works **perfectly,** all the time. No uncertainty.

    If you have a lamp not giving good results, send for a Bystrom, Burner, with gallery, and you will be pleased.
    Price ....$ 2.75

Write for discount.

Can Openers

No. 5,   Steel Blade, polished wood handle, per dozen............... $2.00
Packed 1 dozen in a paper box ; 1 gross in a case.

Steak Pounders

No. 1, Steak pounder, all iron, white plate finish, per dozen........$ 1.50
2, Steak pounder, all iron, nickel plated, per dozen.............. 3.00
Packed 1 dozen each in a paper box.

No. 3, Steak pounder, wood handle varnished, head white plated,
per dozen, ...$ 2.00
4, Steak pounder, wood handle varnished, head nickel plated,
per dozen.. 4.00

Packed ½ dozen in a paper box.

Write for discount.

No. 141—Walker's Quick and Easy Potato Masher

PATENT TO BE APPLIED FOR.

Measurement—Height, 27¼ in., width, 21½ in., depth, 16 in.   Net weight, 36 lbs.

Price, complete, each.......................................$37.00

Write for discount.

IT is designed for mashing potatoes and other vegetables, in Hotels, Restaurants, Hospitals, &c., where large quantities are used. It is quick and easy to operate, so that the vegetables have no time to cool, thus allowing the steam to expand them, dry and mealy.

To OPERATE.—The cooked vegatables are dumped into the hopper as they come from the steamer. The operator then works the lever up and down, mashing the vegetables through between tinned steel bars into pan below.

The hopper is constructed so the vegetables will not clog, but fill the masher each time the lever is worked up and down, until all are mashed. There is no waste as the masher cleans itself, which is a very important consideration in comparison with the waste in other machines, which, with the great saving in time, will soon pay for the masher.

As the operator is out of the steam and from over the machine, no drops of perspiration can fall into the mashed vegetables as is the case with other appliances now in use. As all parts of the masher that come in contact with the vegetables are heavily tinned, there is no discoloration.

All working parts are quickly removed for cleaning.

Capacity, about one bushel per minute.

The Elgin Butter Cutter

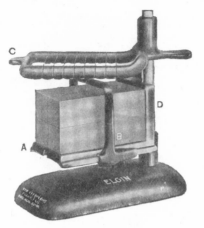

Description.

Used for cutting brick butter into neat, clean, individual serving pieces, quickly and without waste.

Made of solid brass, finely polished and heavily nickel plated. The cutting wires are of the best silver steel piano wire, and guaranteed to last. Nothing about the device to rust, tarnish or break.

Dimensions: The base is 8 in. long, 4½ in. wide, stands 9 in. high, weighs 6 lbs.

A fact not generally known ; and you may not believe it until you try it yourself, viz : The Elgin Butter Cutter will cut enough more individual pieces of butter from the same number of pounds of brick butter of the same size as the molded forms made from tub butter, to more than pay the difference in cost between brick and tub butter, not mentioning the other special advantages of using brick butter.

Explanation :—When you mold the individual piece you not only spoil the grain but you compress the butter.

An Elgin Butter Cutter.—Business Proposition.

1.—You can make a saving in labor alone sufficient to cover the cost of investment in one month's time.

2.—Add to your profits every month hereafter the equivalent of the cost of investment.

3.—Increase your patronage by the better manner in which the investment enables you to serve your customers.

By an investment of $10.00 for one of our Elgin Butter Cutters :

The original grain of the butter is preserved in the individual pieces. This and the fine appearance of the squares makes the improved service a patronage increasing proposition.

Sizes

No. 0 cuts 24 individual pieces, 1¼ in. square by 11-16 in. thick from a standard 1 lb. brick.

No. 1 cuts 28 individual pieces 1¼ in. square by ½ in. thick from a standard 1 lb. brick.

No. 2 cuts 32 individual pieces 1¼ in. square, by 7-16 in. thick, from a standard 1 lb. brick.

No. 3 cuts 32 individual pieces 1¼ in. square, by 3-8 in. thick, from a standard 1 lb. brick.

No. 4 cuts 48 individual pieces 1¼ in. square, by 5-16 in. thick from a standard 1 lb. brick.

Price, each..$12.75

Write for discount.

No. 1—Satin Wine Cooler

Plain Wine Cooler with bright hoops. Substantially made. Extra heavy, best quadruple plate.

Price, each $13.75

No. 2—Wine Cooler

Grape Pattern Wine Cooler, satin finish, with bright bands.   Extra well made.

Price, each........................ ....$13.75

Write for discount.

Nickel-Plated House Numbers

3-inch Oval Figure   3-inch Flat Figure

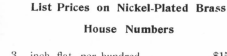

List Prices on Nickel-Plated Brass
House Numbers

3	inch. flat, per hundred		..............$15.50
2½	" "	"	.... 13.75
2	" "	"	.... 12.75
1½	" "	"	.... 9.50
1	" "	"	.... 9.00
½	" "	"	.... 8.25
3	" oval,	"	.... 19.00
2	" "	"	.... 12.75
1½	" "	"	.... 9.50
3	" "	aluminum, polished, per 100.	21.75

2-inch Oval Figure.

Iron House Numbers

3 nch., Nickel-plated, per hundred ....$ 7.25

Write for discount.

All Copper Nickel=Plated Bottle Caps

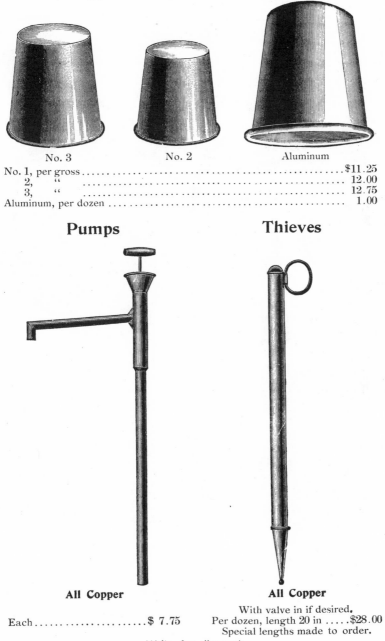

No. 3	No. 2	Aluminum

```
No. 1, per gross ..................................................... $11.25
  2,   "    ..................................................... 12.00
  3,   "    ..................................................... 12.75
Aluminum, per dozen ............................................. 1.00
```

Pumps

All Copper

Each .... $ 7.75

Write for discount.

Thieves

All Copper

With valve in if desired.
Per dozen, length 20 in $28.00
Special lengths made to order.

ICE   SCOOP

Nickel-Plated or Copper.   Length, 8½ inches.

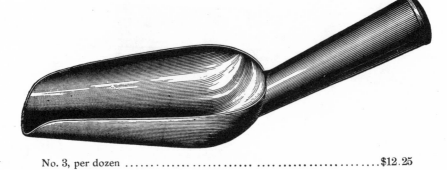

No. 3, per dozen $12.25

Heavy Nickel Ice Scoop

This Scoop is made with a brace underneath the handle, which makes it the strongest Scoop on the market.

No. 295, per dozen $12.50

Copper   Scoop

No. 191, per dozen ....$ 9.25

Tin   Scoop

No. 291, per dozen ....$ 6.25

Write for discount.

There are just three kinds of Cleaners the ordinary kind, the bad kind and

Yankee Cleaner

There are about as many other Cleaners in the market which are as satisfactory as YANKEE CLEANER as there are crocodiles in Greenland—that's none.

It's an honest fact that there are too many Cleaners in the field.

One is satisfactory for use upon wood-work, but would ruin a carpet. Another will remove dirt or grease spots from carpets or rugs but will destroy a fine handkerchief. Still another will clean a brass sign but will utterly spoil a straw hat, and so on through the whole catalogue.

The YANKEE CLEANER is the only one which may be used everywhere, and which invariably gives satisfaction.

It is economical. This means that twenty-five cents' worth of YANKEE CLEANER will do more cleaning and better cleaning than twenty-five cents' worth of any other kind of Cleaner.

It is easy to use. This means that it removes dirt without hard physical labor.   The Cleaner itself is full of muscle.

About all the labor in any kind of cleaning is the scrubbing and scouring. YANKEE CLEANER reduces this by more than half, and polishes without scratching.

The YANKEE CLEANER contains no poison, acid or other injurious substance. It is the embodiment of PURITY.

Cleans everything
but a guilty conscience.

Pint cans, each	$ 0.35
Quart " "	0.65
Gallon cans, each	1.75
Barrel, per gallon	1.50

Write for discount.

BRASS CHECKS
Cuts Full Size

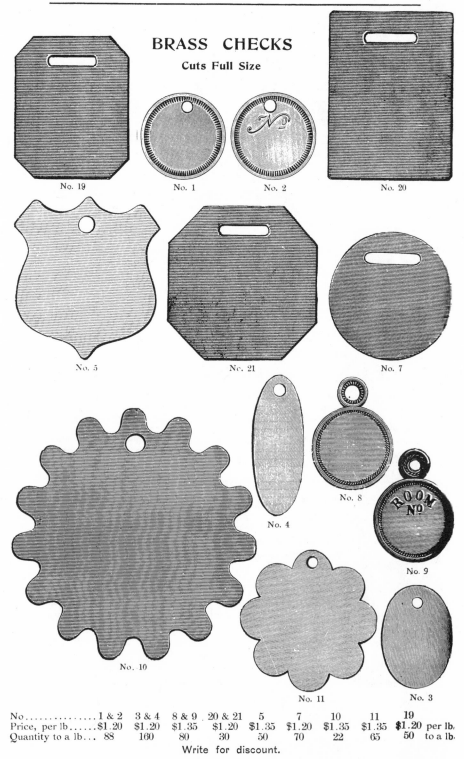

No. 19   No. 1   No. 2   No. 20

No. 5   Nc. 21   No. 7

No. 10   No. 4   No. 8   No. 9   No. 11   No. 3

No.	1 & 2	3 & 4	8 & 9	20 & 21	5	7	10	11	19	
Price, per lb	$1.20	$1.20	$1.35	$1.20	$1.35	$1.20	$1.35	$1.35	$1.20	per lb.
Quantity to a lb	88	160	80	30	50	70	22	65	50	to a lb.

Write for discount.

Beer Hose Protector

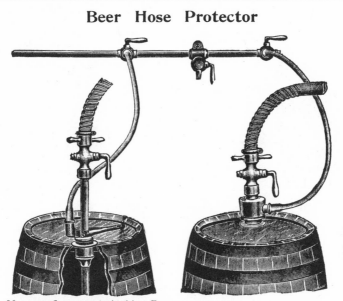

No more flat, spongy looking Beer.
No more tying up Hose with strings or wire.
No more breaks during rush hours.
No more kinks and leaky Hose or wasting of Beer.
No saloon can be without it.

The above cut represents the Patent Beer Hose Protector and Clamp, complete. No saloon can afford to be without one on each tap ; it holds the Hose straight and firm, thereby leaving a least obstruction in the pipes, such as kink in the hose, will make the Beer draw foamy, and after it is drawn in the glass, the foam shows small beads and looks spongy, where it should show a rich creamy white foam. It is simple in construction and cannot get out of order, and will last for years.

Price, per dozen .... $ 6.25

Spray Nozzle

This pipe is superior to all other spray pipes on the market. It is highly finished and of shapely proportions, appealing at first sight to the novice or unexperienced user, while a close examination reveals to the expert the simplicity of its parts and the accuracy of its construction.

There are but three pieces to the whole pipe, none of which are fragile ; and the screw, water-way and base, being all in one piece, insure a satisfactory and reliable adjustment.

Price, each .... $ 7.00

Write for discount. 8

Bung Starts No. 1

Selected Hickory Heads, Second Growth Hickory Handles.
Standard Pattern

No. 1—Dovetailed Heads, with screws, per dozen ....$ 4.60

Bung Starts No. 2

Selected Hickory Heads, Second Growth Hickory Handles.
Improved Pattern

No. 2 —Mortised Heads, Handles securely wedged and riveted at end,
per dozen...$ 7.75

MALLETS

Mortised Handles

No. 8—Square Hickory, 6	in. long, 2½ x 3½ in., per dozen........$ 3.00
9— " " 6½ " " 2¾ x 3¾ " " 3.75
10— " " 7 " " 3 x 4 " " 4.50
11— " Lignum-Vitae, 6 in. long, 2½ x 3½ in., " 5.75
12— " " " 6½ " " 2¾ x 3¾ " " 7.25
13— " " " 7 " " 3 x 4 " " 9.00

Write for discount.

Enterprise Ice Shredders

Nos. 33 and 34—For Shaving Ice Coarse or Fine

The mode of operation requires no explanation, being simply to draw the blade upon a piece of ice—the pressure applied producing fine or coarse pieces as desired.   To remove the finely cut ice from the cup, grasp the shredder firmly in the right hand and strike it, inverted, upon the left, at the same time being careful to keep the Lid close.   Then scrape the ice into some convenient receptacle.   It is not necessary to take the ice out of the refrigerator, the cup can be filled from the side, end or top of a cake of ice without disturbing anything or wetting the hands.   Its use will be appreciated when icing Fruits, Drinks, Oysters and Clams on the half shell, Olive, Celery, Radishes, Tea, Sliced Tomatoes, etc., and for many purposes in the sick room.

No. 33, Tinned, per dozen.....................................$13.50

34, Nickeled, per dozen................................... 34.50

No. 43—Shredder

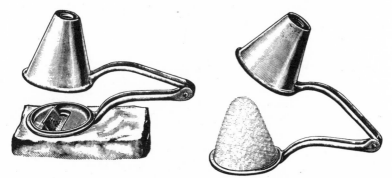

The No. 43 Shredder differs from the No. 33 only in shape and the balde being placed in the Lid instead of bottom of bowl.   After the shredder is scraped full of ice, tap the small end of cone so as to make contents solid. It is especially adapted for the use of vendors selling " Snow Balls, " as by the hole in the small end of cone, the ball can be readily flavored and easily ejected.

Price, per dozen...$20.50

Write for discount.

No. 210 and No. 211—Walker's Quick and Easy Champagne Tap

Sectional view showing construction.

A German silver wire is secured to the valve screw extending and closing the reduced opening in point of tap, which prevents clogging with small parts of cork.   On this wire at end of valve screw is a vulcanized fibre washer with sufficient resiliancy to make the valve gas and liquid tight.

When valve is opened the wire is drawn back from point leaving a free opening around it for flow of contents.

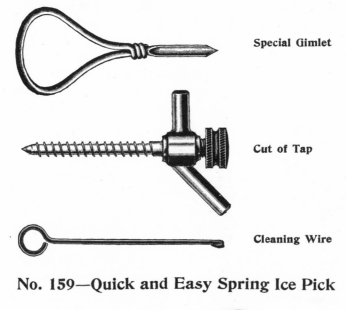

Special Gimlet

Cut of Tap

Cleaning Wire

No. 159—Quick and Easy Spring Ice Pick

No. 159

Write for discount.

No. 210—Walker's Champagne Tap

1904 Design

Patented February 4, 1902.   Other Patents allowed.

HE only Gas Tight and complete outfit for drawing Champagne and other Carbonated Beverages. The last drop is drawn with gas pressure when bottles have been on tap for days or months and drawn in small quantities as required.   This new design is a great departure from old ideas.   Its construction prevents leakage of gas or contents and clogging, with cork.   The valve screw when removed leaves all parts accessible for thorough cleaning, making it the only sanitary tap ever produced.

Physicians and nurses for use in hospitals and the sick room, as well as others, will appreciate its great value as compared with the imperfect taps of the past that clog with cork and leak the contents.

With No. 210 is one Tap, one special steel Gimlet, with a stop shoulder, which allows it to only penetrate the tin cap and hard part of cork sufficiently to allow the tap to be easily inserted without removing cap or wire, which is important ; one Cleaning Wire and one Walker Quick and Easy Spring Ice Pick No. 159 wedge pointed, finely tempered steel, for cracking small pieces of ice.

No. 210 Tap, Gimlet, Ice Pick and Wire Cleaner are all finely nickeled and packed one in a wood box.

Price, per set....................................$ 2.00

No. 211, same as above, without Ice Pick.

Price, per set....................................$ 1.60

Write for discount.

No. 178—Walker's Quick and Easy Ice Cream Disher

Seamless pressed copper cup, nickel plated, German silver knives, malleable iron handle, anti-rust nickel plated. Will not rust, wear out or color the cream, making it the most sanitary disher on the market. Operated with one hand. Made in five sizes. Correct measure.

	PRICE					
Size to the quart	16	12	10	8	6	5
Dozen,	$31.00	$31.00	$33.00	$33.00	$35.00	$37.00

Cigar Box Opener

Nickel plated, per dozen ....$ 1.50

Coppered,   " 0.60

Packed 1 dozen in a paper box.

Write for discount.

Chafing   Dishes

This Chafing Dish is made of heavy copper throughout, heavily tinned inside, highly finished and nickel-plated.   It has separate compartment for water with a pan or tray to hold contents.

This article can be used as a Chafing Dish and Hot Water Urn combined.

Size, 11 x 16, each $29.00
    11 x 18, " 35.00
    12 x 20, " 41.00
    12 x 22, " 47.00
    12 x 24, " 53.00

Write for discount.

Food Warmer

This Food Warmer is made of heavy copper throughout, heavily tinned inside, highly finished and nickel-plated. It has separate compartments for different foods. Sixteen and 18 inch have only two compartments ; 20, 22 and 24 have three.

This article can be used as a Chafing Dish and Hot Water Urn combined.

Size, 11 x 16, each $29.00
     11 x 18, " 35.00
     12 x 20, " 41.00
     12 x 22, " 47.00
     12 x 24, " 53.00

Write for discount.

Hot Water Urns

Made from 20 oz. stock.   All Copper, Nickel-Plated

No. 2042, 2 gallon, each $21.00

2043, 3 "   " 24.00

2044, 4 "   " 26.50

To heat this Urn, see pages 146, 147 and 148.

Write for discount.

Hot Water Urns

Made from 20 oz. stock.   All Copper, Nickel-Plated

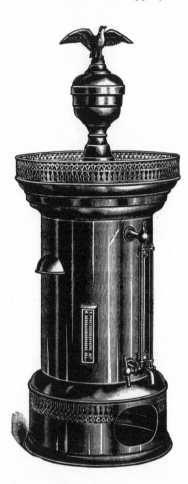

No. 2052, 2 gallon, each..$16.50

2053, 3   "   " 19.50

2054, 4   "   " 22.50

This Urn is placed upon the market with the belief that its superiority of finish and general arrangement will appeal at once to the purchaser.

To heat this Urn, see pages 146, 147 and 148.

Write for discount.

Hot Water Urns

Silver or Nickel-Plated.   Made in one and two gallon sizes

No. 2066, 1 gallon, nickel-plated, each $23.50

2067, 2   "   "   "   " 26.50

2068, 1   "   silver-plated,   " 30.50

2069, 2   "   "   "   " 35.00

Write for discount.

Hot Water Urns

All Copper, Nickel-Plated

No. 2072, 2 gallon, each $12.50

2073, 3 "   " 14.00

2074, 4 "   " 15.50

To heat this Urn, see pages 146, 147 and 148.

Write for discount.

Hot Water Urns

All Copper, Nickel-Plated

No. 3012, 2 gallon, each $11.00

    3013, 3   "   " 12.50

    3014, 4   "   " 14.00

To heat this Urn, see pages 146, 147 and 148.

Write for discount.

Hot Water Urns

All Copper, Nickel-Plated

No. 3032, 2 gallon, each $11.00

3033, 3   "   " 12.50

3034, 4   "   " 14.00

To heat this Urn, see pages 146, 147 and 148.

Write for discount.

Hot Water Urns

Made from Heavy Stock, Nickel-Plated. Beautifully finished, with Lever Handle Faucet

No. 2082, 2 gallon, each $18.00

2083, 3   "   " 21.00

2084, 4   "   " 24.00

To heat this Urn, see pages 146, 147 and 148.

Write for discount.

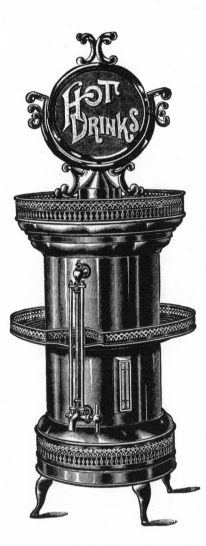

This cut shows a fancy top for Hot Water Urns which can be placed on all Hot Water Urns of our make, and is made from ruby glass. Very showy and ornamental.

Each..$ 6.00

Write for discount.

Double Deck Hot Water Urns
Made from 20 oz. Copper, Tinned on inside, highly finished, and Nickel-Plated outside.

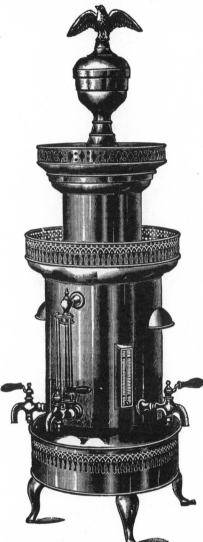

With Lever Handle Gauge Cock, and two Lever Handle Faucets.

Upper section has Lever Handle Faucet, and very convenient for two or more dispensers.

No. 4062, 2 gallon, each $26.50	No. 4065, 5 gallon, each $35.00
4063, 3 " " 29.50	4066, 6 " " 37.50
4064, 4 " " 32.00	

To heat this Urn, see pages 146, 147 and 148.

Write for discount.   9

Double Deck Hot Water Urns

All Copper, Nickel-Plated.   Made from 20 oz. stock.   Upper section has Lever Handle Faucet.

```
No. 2062, 2 gallon, each .............................................$23.00
    2063, 3   "      "    ............................................ 26.00
    2064, 4   "      "    ............................................ 28.50
    2065, 5   "      "    ............................................ 31.25
```

To heat this Urn, see pages 146, 147 and 148.

Write for discount.

All Copper and Nickel Urns

Made from 20 Oz. Stock

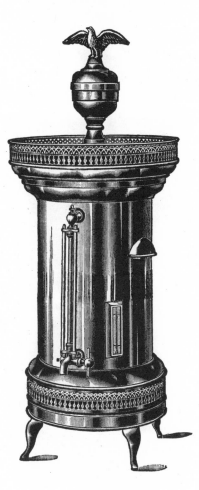

No. 2022, 2 gallon, each...$17.00

2023, 3 gallon, each... 19.50

2024, 4 gallon, each... 22.00

To heat this Urn, see pages 146, 147 and 148.

Write for discount.

Hot Water Urns

All Copper, Nickel-Plated

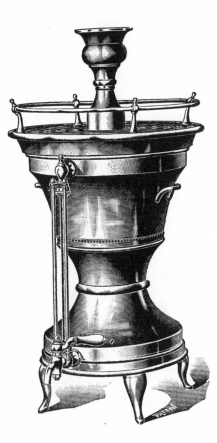

Made from 24 oz. stock, spun throughout, making it the best and finest Urn in the market.

No. 1422, each...$28.00

1423, each... 30.50

To heat this Urn, see pages 146, 147 and 148.

Write for discount.

Hot Water Urns

All Copper, Nickel-Plated

Made from 24 oz. stock, spun throughout, making it the best and finest Urn in the market.

No. 1402, each..$28.00

1403, each... 30.50

To heat this Urn, see pages 146, 147 and 148.

Write for discount.

Water Coolers

Nickel-Plated, All Copper

Galvanized iron lined, charcoal filled ; has self-closing faucet.

No. 4002, 2 gallon, each $22.00
    4003, 3 gallon, each.. 23.50
    4004, 4 gallon, each.. 25.00
    4005, 5 gallon, each.. 26.50
    4006, 6 gallon, each.. 28.00
    4008, 8 gallon, each.. 29.50
    4010, 10 gallon, each.. 31.00

Write for discount.

"New Era" Water Cooler

Reservoir and Ice Cylinder.   Porcelain Lined.   Nickel Plated Self-Closing Faucet.   With separate reservoir for ice, which avoids all chance of water becoming contaminated by using impure ice.

This Cooler is painted, decorated or lettered, as desired, without any extra charge.

No.	Capacity Ice	Water	Extreme Height	Diameter Base	Weight Boxed	Price each
512	26 lbs.	8 gals.,	34 in.,	19¼ in.,	160 lbs.	$54.50
514	26 lbs.	10 "	36 "	20 "	180 "	62.25
516	35 lbs.	11 "	38 "	20½ "	270 "	85.50
520	35 lbs.	15 "	40 "	21½ "	300 "	103.00

Write for discount.

Battery of Hot Soda Urns

This consists of two 3 gallon Urns and one 5 gallon Boiler, all connected with necessary pipes and valves. Can be furnished with steam coil pipes for steam heat at small advance in price.

Per set...................................... ....$231.00

Write for discount.

Soda Urns

No bottles or glasses included in the prices.   Other sizes furnished if desired.   To heat this Urn, see pages 146, 147 and 148.

No. 1703, 3 gallon, each...$33.50

1704, 4 gallon, each.. 39.00

1705, 5 gallon, each.. 44.50

Write for discount.

Soda Urn

No bottles or glasses included in this price. Other sizes furnished if desired.   For heating this Urn, see pages 146, 147 and 148.

No. 1713, 3 gallon, each..................................$44.50

Write for discount.

Hot Chocolate Urns

With Vitrified Stone or Block Tin Reservoir. This Urn is arranged so the chocolate may be stirred without removing the cover.

Please state in ordering whether Block Tin or Vitrified Stone Reservoir is wanted. For heating this Urn, see pages 146, 147 and 148.

No. 1802, 2 gallon, each....................................$53.00
1803, 3 gallon, each.... .... 59.50
1804, 4 gallon, each................................... 66.00
1805, 5 gallon, each................................... 72.50
1806, 6 gallon, each................................... 79.00
1808, 8 gallon, each................................... 86.00

Write for discount.

Coffee or Tea Urn

Vitrified stone reservoir on inside for tea or coffee with textile filter for coffee ; outer shell made from copper, nickel-plated, tinned on inside, which surrounds coffee reservoir. Lever handle faucets and gauge to show water. Also has alcohol lamp, which can be removed if desired. Made only in one size.

No. 2261, 1 gallon, each...................................$41.00

Write for discount.

Coffee or Tea Urn

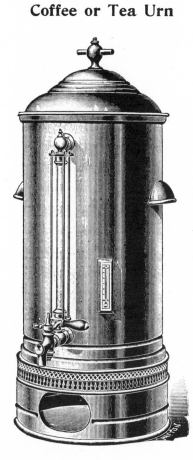

Nickel-plated, made of heavy copper, tinned on inside with pure block tin, and satin finished.   Has textile filter for the coffee.   Base attached to body of Urn, or made with loose base if desired.

No. 2202,   2 gallon, each...$16.00
　　2203,   3 gallon, each....................................... 18.50
　　2204,   4 gallon, each....   .... 21.00
　　2205,   5 gallon, each....................................... 23.50
　　2206,   6 gallon, each....................................... 26.00
　　2208,   8 gallon, each....................................... 29.00
　　2210, 10 gallon, each....................................... 32.00
　　2212, 12 gallon, each....................................... 34.50
　　2215, 15 gallon, each....................................... 39.50
　　2220, 20 gallon, each....................................... 46.00

To heat this Urn, see pages 146, 147 and 148.

Write for discount.

Coffee Urns
All Copper, Nickel-Plated, with Vitrified Stone Reservoir

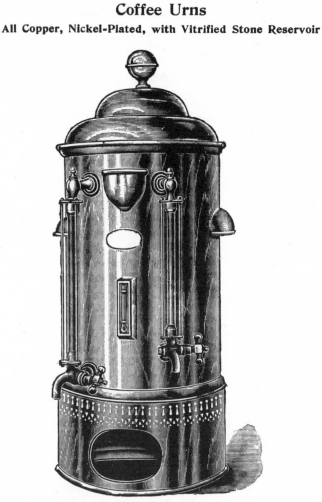

Made from extra heavy copper, nickel-plated, heavy tinned on inside with pure block tin, outside heavily nickel-plated, and finely finished. Fitted with our new style clean-out lever handle gauges ; screw clamp for fastening the gauges to the Urn, one gauge showing the amount of coffee in Urn, the other showing the amount of water between the coffee reservoir and outside shell ; coffee reservoir entirely surrounded by water. We furnish this style of Urn in sizes up to 25 gallons. They can be provided with steam coil pipes for heating the water between the walls when specially ordered. For description of burner suitable for heating this Urn, see pages 146, 147 and 148.

No. 2002, 2 gallon, each....$48.25	No. 2010, 10 gallon, each....$ 85.50
2003, 3 gallon, each.... 53.00	2012, 12 gallon, each.... 92.50
2004, 4 gallon, each.... 59.50	2015, 15 gallon, each.... 102.00
2005, 5 gallon, each.... 66.00	2018, 18 gallon, each.... 112.00
2006, 6 gallon, each.... 72.50	2020, 20 gallon, each.... 119.00
2008, 8 gallon, each.... 79.00	2025, 25 gallon, each.... 132.00

Write for discount.

Coffee and Milk Urn

Made up the same as the No. 2002 series, excepting with the addition of a reservoir for milk

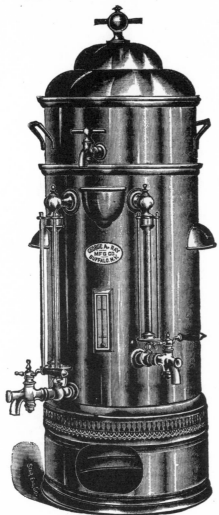

No. 1602, 2 gallon, each....$53.00	No. 1610, 10 gallon, each.... $ 92.50
1603, 3 gallon, each.... 59.50	1612, 12 gallon, each.... 99.00
1604, 4 gallon, each.... 66.00	1615, 15 gallon, each.... 109.00
1605, 5 gallon, each.... 72.50	1618, 18 gallon, each.... 119.00
1606, 6 gallon, each.... 79.50	1620, 20 gallon, each.... 125.50
1608, 8 gallon, each.... 86.00	1625, 25 gallon, each.... 138.00

We make large sizes if desired.   For burner suitable for this Urn, see pages
146, 147 and 148. Reservoir for Coffee, vitrified stone. Upper section for milk.

Write for discount.

Clam Broth Urn

All Copper, Nickel-Plated

This Urn has a vitrified stone reservoir and drainer, with one gauge for drawing off and showing the amount of water, and one cock for drawing off the clam juice. The stone lining we put in this Urn is the only thing known that will withstand the severity of the juice of the clams, as it will even perforate copper in a very short time.

No. 3, 3 gallon, each..$44.00

To heat this Urn, see pages 146, 147 and 148.

Write for discount.

All Copper and Nickel=Plated Urns

Made from 20 Oz. Stock

Solid Stamped Top and Bottom

No. 2032, 2 gallon, each...$17.00
2033, 3 gallon, each... 19.50
2034, 4 gallon, each............. .... 22.50

To heat this Urn, see pages 146, 147 and 148.

The Lightning Burner

PATENT APPLIED FOR

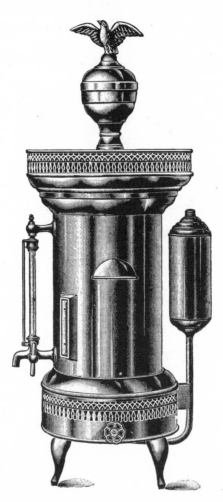

This Urn shows our new heating device attached.   It has been long-felt want among the manufacturers of Urns to find a heating device that would give as good result as gas.   The above is equal in every respect, and the cost would be about one-fourth to that of gas.   Use nothing but the very best gasoline.   Works the same as a gasoline stove.   The device can be easily attached to any Urn we make.

For prices, see pages 147 and 148.

No. 0 Lightning Burner

Small size for heating hot water Urns

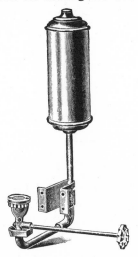

Nickel-plated, each...$4.25

No. 0½

Lightning Burner

Large size for heating Coffee Urns

Nickel-plated, each...............$6.30

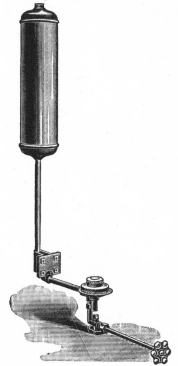

Use nothing but first quality of gasoline. If flame should be irregular, remove feed pipe and put in new wicking. If leak occurs around valve, tighten the stuffing-box slightly with wrench. Always keep burner clean.

Write for discount.

No. 1 Vapor Lamp

No. 2—Gasoline Vapor Lamp

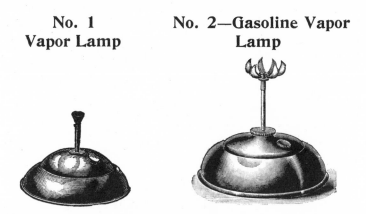

No. 1, Lamp is suitable for all hot water Urns of our manufacture up to 3 gallons and will heat as quickly as gas ; five cents per day will run it ; nothing invented as good.

Per dozen................................$12.75

No. 2, Gasoline Vapor Lamp, the most economical heater in the market. Size, 6¼ in. diameter, 5 in. high. Six Jet Burner, nickel-plated.

Per dozen................................$16.50

Gem Burner

For Gas

Gem Burner

With Lugs, for Gas

No. 1, per dozen $7.75

2, per dozen, with lugs 9.00

Write for discount.

Copper or Nickel=Plated Urns

Crescent Shape for Barbers

Copper

No. 3062, 2 gallon, each... $4.00
    3063, 3 gallon, each.. 4.75
    3064, 4 gallon, each.. 5.50

Nickel-Plated

No. 3072, 2 gallon, each................................... .... $5.00
    3073, 3 gallon, each.. 5.50
    3074, 4 gallon, each.. 6.25

Write for discount.

Copper and Nickel-Plated Urn

Crescent Shape

No. 2092, 7 in. high ; 14 in. diameter............................ $8.50

All Copper and Nickel-Plated Tumbler Drainers

Size 10 x 15, each... $ 7.75
12 x 18, each.. 10.75
12 x 24, each.. 14.00
14 x 30, each.. .... 18.50

Write for discount.

Drip Cup—For Urns

Price, nickel-plated, each....... .... $1.50

Urn Foot Rest

Nickel-Plated

Prevents the marring of the counter or the bar, and adds greatly to the beauty and elegance of the Urn.

1½ inch x ¾ inch high.

Per Set of 4 Rests.. $1.50

Write for discount.

Just What You Need

The cost is but a trifle compared with the saving.

75 per cent. of Matches saved

It comprises ornamentability as well as usefulness.

Those who have one would not part with it for double its cost.

It will hold 5 packages of matches, thus saving you the trouble of constantly filling up your match holder as is the case with the ordinary match holders.

Nickel Plated, each.. $2.60
Oxidized, each.. 3.00

Write for discount.

No Charge for Packages

002-8oz.   003—9oz.   003—12oz.   309—8oz.

305—7oz.   403—13oz.   402—14o-   091—13 oz.

FRICTION RUBBER FOR 48½   No.125

001—11½oz.   200—12½oz.   290   RUBBER CUSHION   No.124

No.								
No. 002— 8 oz. Light Bell Top, lead glass							$ 1.70	per dozen
003— 9 oz.	"	"	"	"	"		1.85	"
003—12 oz.	"	"	"	"	"		2.50	"
309— 8 oz.	"	Mineral	"	"			1.70	"
305— 7 oz.	"	"	"	"			1.70	"
403—13 oz. Medium Soda		"	"				2.50	"
402—14 oz. Light		"	"	"			2.70	"
091—13 oz. Pressed Soda							1.90	"
001—12 oz. Bell Top, Pressed Soda							2.10	"
200—12½ oz. Pressed Soda or Lemonade, used on Shakers							1.80	"
290—Glass Caps for Milk Shakers							3.10	"
124—Aluminum Cap for Shakers							18.50	"
291—Rubber Cushions for Glass or Aluminum Caps							3.10	"
125—Rubber Friction for No. 48½ Shaker							5.50	"

Write for discount.

No. 11124—2½ oz.

Price, per dozen..........$ 0.90

No. 20123—1½ oz.

Price, per dozen..........$ 0.90

No. 10524—3 oz.

Price, per dozen..........$ 0.70

No. 20327—2 oz.

Price, per dozen........$ 0.90

Write for discount.

No. 10021—2 oz.

Price, per dozen...........$ 0.60

No. 10122—2¼ oz.

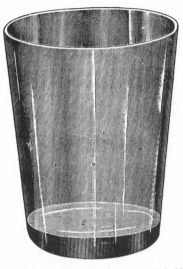

Price, per dozen..........$ 0.60

No. 10222—2½ oz.

Price, per dozen...........$ 0.60

No. 10323—2¾ oz.

Price, per dozen..........$ 0.60

Write for discount.

No. 10424—2¾ oz.   No. 10930—2¼ oz.

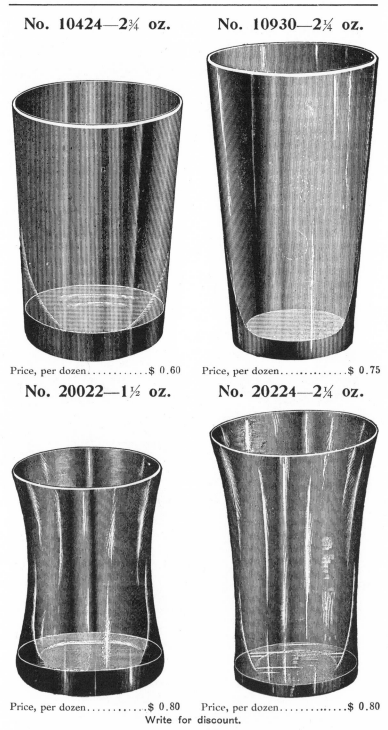

Price, per dozen............$ 0.60   Price, per dozen.............$ 0.75

No. 20022—1½ oz.   No. 20224—2¼ oz.

Price, per dozen............$ 0.80   Price, per dozen..............$ 0.80

Write for discount.

No. 20531—   oz.   No. 20527—3 oz.

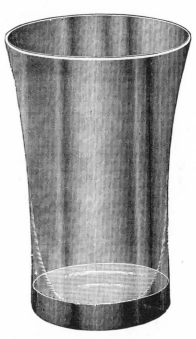

Price, per dozen............$ 0.80   Price, per dozen............$ 0.80

No. 20424— 2 oz.

Price, per
dozen. $0.80

Write for discount.

No. 40136—4 oz.

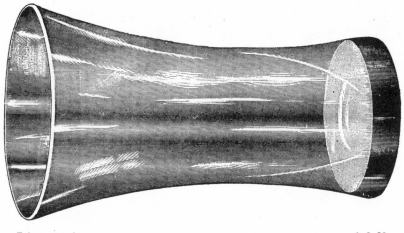

Price, per dozen,..$ 0.80

No. 40237—4¾ oz.

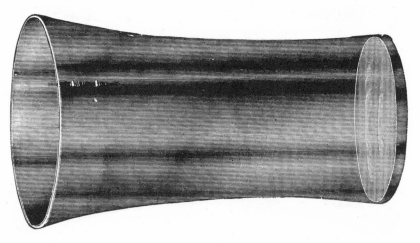

Price, per dozen..$ 0.80

Write for discount.

No. 40645--5¼ oz.

Price, per dozen. . . . .$ 0.90

No. 40741--7¼ oz.

Price, per dozen. . . . .$ 1.00

Write for discount.

No. 40341—7½ oz.

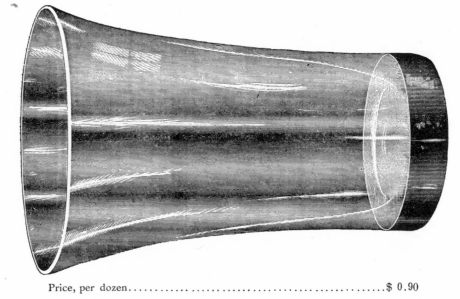

Price, per dozen...$ 0.90

No. 50135—5 oz.

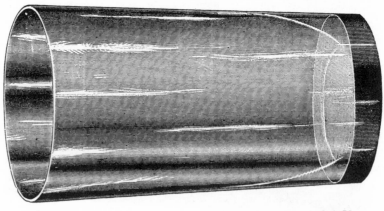

Price, per dozen.......................................$ 0.75

Write for discount.

No. 50240—7 oz.

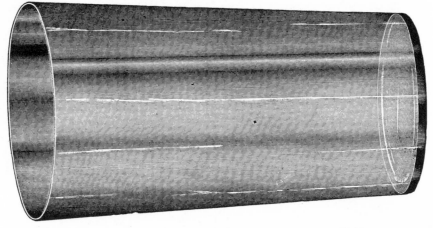

Price, per dozen..$0.82

No. 50343—9 oz.

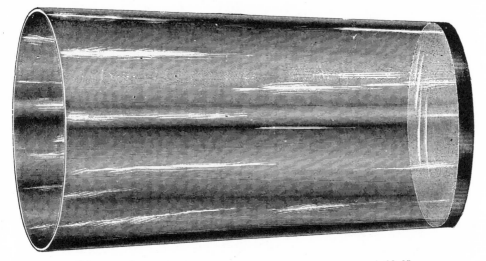

Price, per dozen..$0.85

No. 80046—12 oz.

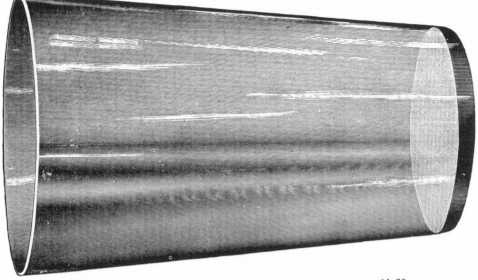

Price, per dozen $1.20

No. 60436—9 oz.

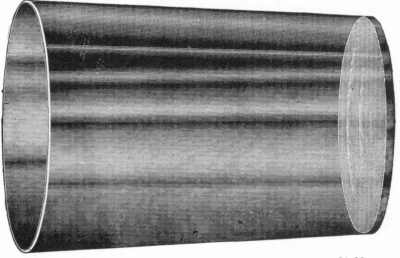

Price, per dozen $1.00

Write for discount.

No. 50444—8½ oz.

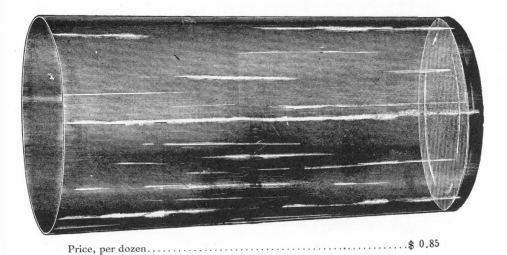

Price, per dozen..$ 0.85

No. 60540—8½ oz.

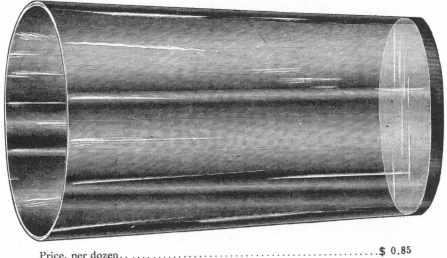

Price, per dozen..$ 0.85

Write for discount.

No. 60336—7 oz.

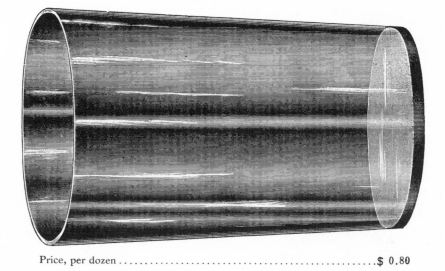

Price, per dozen . . . . $ 0.80

No. 60640—9¼ oz.

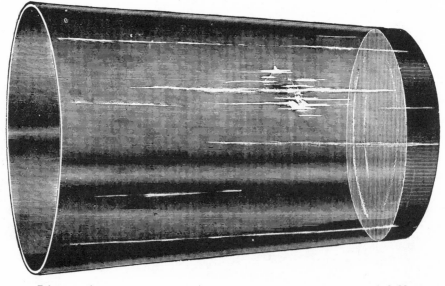

Price, per dozen . . . . $ 0.90

Write for discount.

No. 60742—10½ oz.

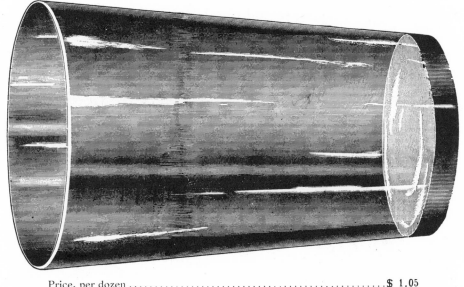

Price, per dozen ....$ 1.05

No. 60842—10½ oz.

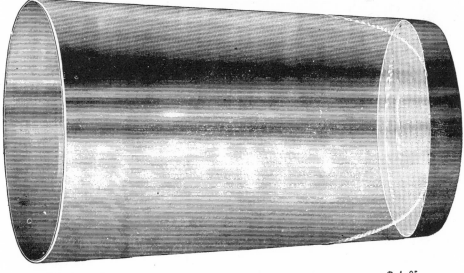

Price, per dozen ....$ 1.05

Write for discount.

No. 70034—4¾ oz.

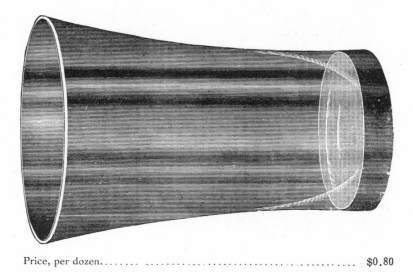

Price, per dozen........ .... $0.80

No. 70135—5½ oz.

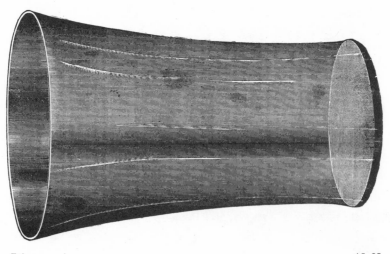

Price, per dozen.. $0.85

Write for discount.

No. 70236—6½ oz.

Price, per dozen.. $0.90

No. 70340—7½ oz.

Price, per dozen.. $0.90

Write for discount.

No. 70541—8½ oz.

Price, per dozen.. $0.95

No. 70543—9½ oz.

Price, per dozen.. $1.05

Write for discount.

No. 70642—9¾ oz.

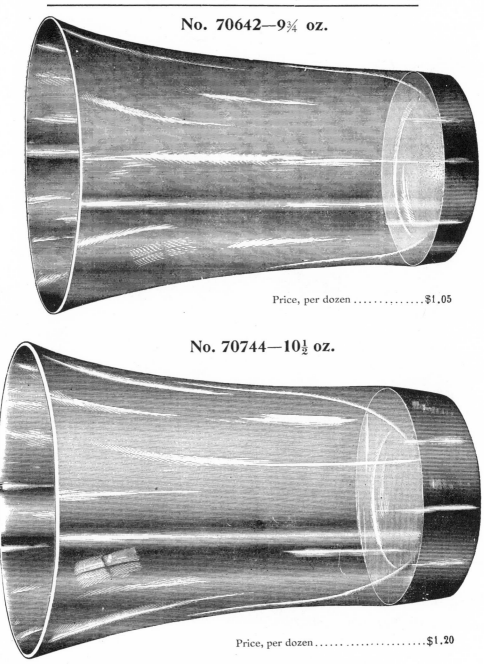

Price, per dozen $1.05

No. 70744—10½ oz.

Price, per dozen $1.20

Write for discount.

No. 70953—12 oz.

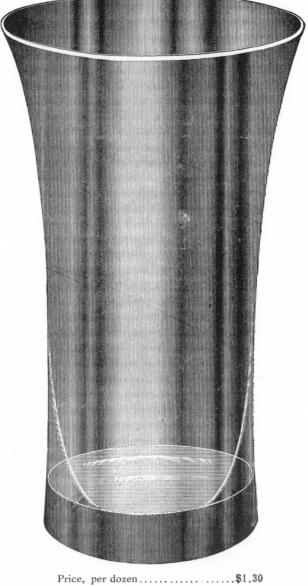

Price, per dozen................. ......$1.30

Write for discount.

No. 80250—12½ oz.

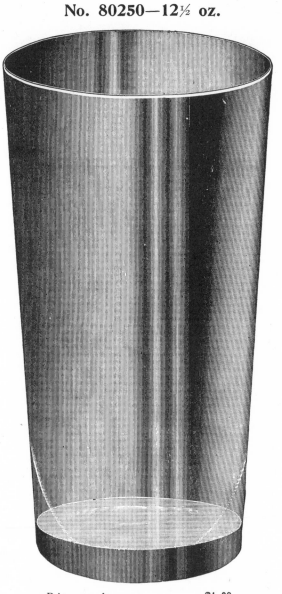

Price, per dozen...............$1.30

Write for discount.

No. 80351—12½ oz.

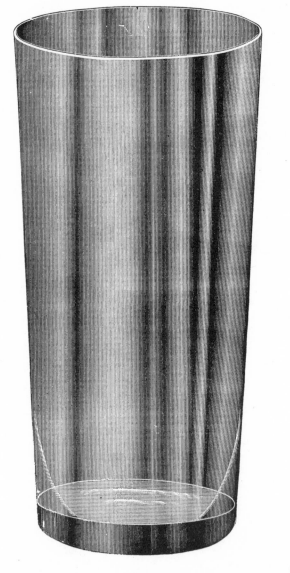

Price, per dozen..$ 1.30

Write for discount.

No. 80560—22 oz.

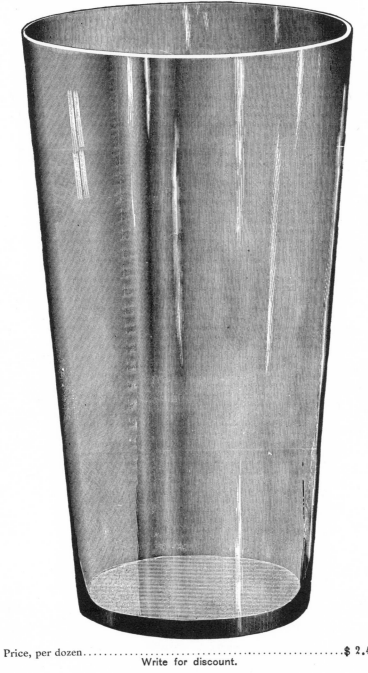

Price, per dozen...$ 2.40
Write for discount.

No. 80450—17 oz.

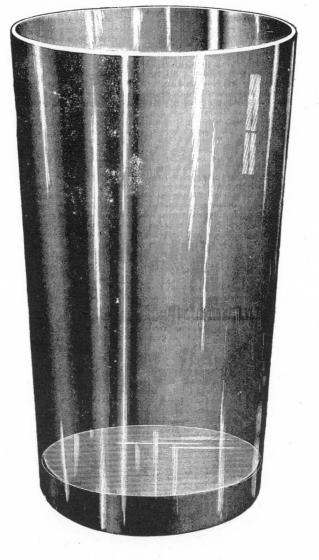

Price per dozen..$ 1.80

Write for discount.

No. 80150—11½ oz.

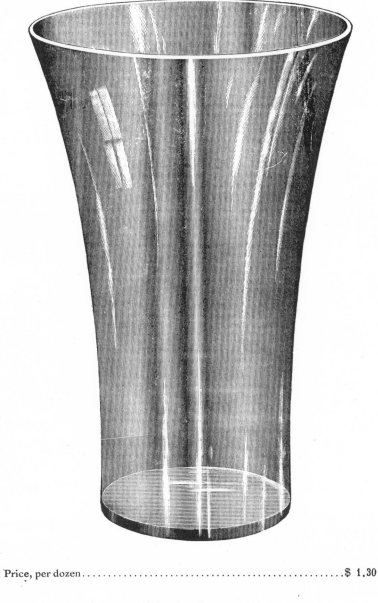

Price, per dozen..$ 1.30

Write for discount.

Automatic Meal Auditor

Valuable for head waiters or kitchen checkers to count number of meals served out of kitchen. Registers up to 999. Count made by simply pressing lever, as shown in illustration, which then springs back to place. Small enough to be held in palm of hand.

Price, each............................ $7.00

SIPHON

Best Bohemian Glass Bottle and Pure Block Tin
Siphon Heads

28 oz., each $1.05
32 oz., each 1.20
44 oz., each 1.40

Write for discount.

COCKTAILS

No. 4429—3½ oz.   No. 4438— 2¾ oz.   No. 4495.

No. 4429, per dozen.. $1.40
    4438,   " 1.40
    4495,   " 1.40

Weise Beers

No. 5305½—29½ oz.   No. 5319—17 oz.

No. 5305½, per dozen.. $5.25
    5319,   " 2.50

Write for discount.   12

Beer—Ale Goblet

Champagne

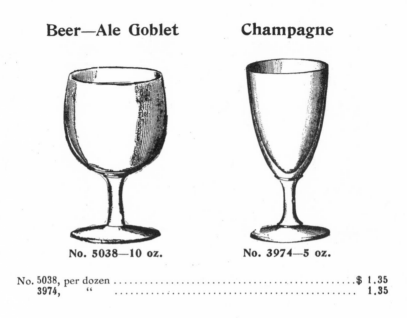

No. 5038—10 oz.   No. 3974—5 oz.

No. 5038, per dozen ....$ 1.35
   3974,   " 1.35

Soda

Tumbler

No. 1236—12½ oz.   No. 1259—11 oz.

No. 1236, per dozen ....$ 1.35
   1259,   " 1.20

Write for discount.

BITTERS

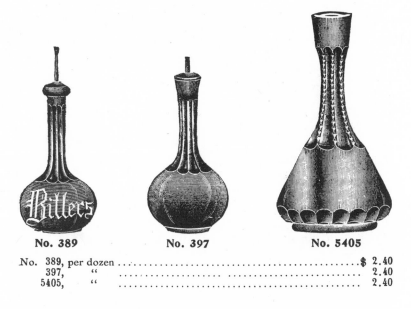

| No. 389 | No. 397 | No. 5405 |

No. 389, per dozen .... $ 2.40
    397,   " 2.40
    5405,   " 2.40

Stone's Patent Paper Lemonade Straws

Every one perfect. 500 to package

**500 Stone's
Paper Julep
Straws.**

No. D 187

Price, per package... $ 0.55

Write for discount.

Shoo Fly — Scant Measures

The best quality Flint Glass

No. 1721—Choke Neck Bar Bottle

Good quality clear glass

½ pint, per box of 6 dozen..$ 2.85
1 "   "   "   " .. 4.40
1 quart,   "   "   " .. 7.25

Per dozen ....$ 7.75

Engraved with any brand of liquor.

No. D 134—Old Style Metal Stopper

With Marble ; Self-closing

No. D 171—Porcelain Mounted Bar Bottle Stopper

All brands of Wine and Liquors

Price, per dozen...........$ 2.30

Price, per dozen ....$ 1.70

Write for discount.

Liquor Bottle Display Stand No. 1

Make a very handsome exhibit either when used in window or back bar. Circular Plate Glass Mirror Top ; seven inches diameter ; beveled and polished edges ; Standard adjustable from 12 to 24 inches ; made of fancy brass tubing, heavily nickel-plated.

Price, each ....$ 5.75

Write for discount.

Wine Bottle Display

Holder No. 3

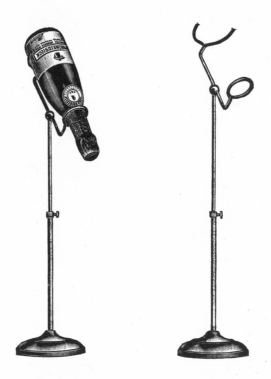

Very attractive when used in connection with No. I Stand. Made of ⅜ in. rod ; heavily nickel-plated : height to top of stand when extended, 22 inches ; made for pints and quarts. In ordering specify size desired.

Price, each...$3.25

Write for discount.

PERFECTION DECANTERS, BOTTLES, Etc.

No. 5329
Perfection Water Bottle

Imitation Cut Glass Water Bottle. Made in two pieces. Neck attached to bowl by heavily plated solid nickel silver ring, producing absolutely water tight connection. All dirt and dust is excluded at connection of parts. However, when open, it allows the bottle to be cleaned as easily as any tumbler or pitcher and large pieces of ice can be placed within.

Price, each..........$0.65

No. 5122
Perfection Vinegar Bottle

It is useless to say much about the merits of this article as same are too apparent. Vinegar discolors glass; it also produces a sediment that is hard to expel from an ordinary bottle. This is all made easy by our perfection.

Price, each..........$0.50
Price, per dozen.......6.00

No. 5328—Perfection Decanter

Imitation Cut Glass Decanter. Made in two pieces. Neck attached to bowl by heavily plated solid nickel silver ring, producing absolutely water tight connection. When closed this decanter is similar in appearance to the very expensive cut glass ones. All dirt and dust is excluded. However, when open, it allows the decanter to be cleaned as easily as any tumbler, and large pieces of ice, fruit, etc., can be placed within.

Price, each..........$0.90

Write for discount.

This Bottle Opener is a Perpetual Reminder

Inexpensive Enough to admit of a Wide Distribution

It's usefulness is a guarantee that it will be much appreciated, and as it is practically indistructible, it makes a permanent advertisement.

Better let us stamp you up a thousand.

Price, per hundred... $ 7.50

"   "   thousand... 62.00

Write for discount.

Is your SILVERWARE in good order?
We plate and repair equal to new.
We do all kinds of SILVER PLATING.
Ask for our prices.
We fear no competition.

Silver Plating:

Table Spoons or Forks........................... $3.00 per dozen, Net.
Desert Spoons or Forks.......................... 2.25 " " "
Tea Spoons..................................... 1.50 " " "
Steel Knives................................... 2.50 " " "

Heavily plated and finished like new.

Why buy a new Cash Register, when you can have yours Nickel-Plated

For $10.00, or Silver-Plated for $15.00, Net.

Noxall Jr. Germ Proof Filters

Made of spun copper top and cast brass bottom, tinned on the inside and highly polished nickel on the outside.

The top is fitted with our improved rubber attachment, which is spun into the shell, making it indestructible and easy to slip onto any faucet (as shown by the cut).

Noxall Jr. is 2x4 inches in size, weighs 12 ounces complete, and filters 5 to 10 gallons of water per hour.

Noxall Jr. is a perfect filter—perfect in construction and workmanship. The filtering medium we use, the germ proof natural Noxall stone, is the same we use in all high price Noxall Filters. Each Filter is packed in a box with full directions.

Noxall Filters

Are perfection in workmanship and finish, are extremely simple, cannot possibly get out of order, and with ordinary care will last a lifetime.

The shells are made of spun copper, nickeled and highly polished on the outside and tinned on the inside. The bases are made of best cast brass, nickeled.

Remember, there is no water like filtered water and no filter like a Noxall.

This cut illustrates how easily the No. 1, 3 and 5 Noxall's are taken apart —No screws, nuts or bolts—No tools necessary.

Noxall Faucet Connection

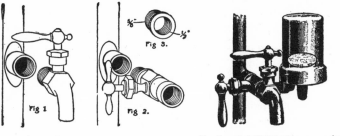

**No. 1 and 3 NOXALL permanently
attached to side of faucet.**

FIG. 1 shows faucet unscrewed from the wall.

FIG. 2 shows connection in position to be screwed into the wall piece.

FIG. 3 shows collar to change connection from ½ in. to ⅝ in. Fuller and *vice versa*, or ½ in. to ¾ in. iron pipe and *vice versa*.

This arrangement does not interfere with the drawing of unfiltered water through the faucet just as before.

The NOXALL connection is extremely simple, easily attached and fits the No. 1 and No. 3 Noxall Filters, both having the same size threads and openings.

When ordering, state whether Fuller or iron pipe thread connection is wanted. To determine this, unscrew your faucet from the wall and count the number of threads there are to the inch. Fuller connection has 20 threads and iron-pipe 14 threads to the inch.

PRICE LIST.

	Each	Extra Stones	Capacity per hour	Weight
Junior Filter	$4.70	$1.15	5 Gals.	12 oz.
No. 1 "	9.25	1.40	10 "	2 lbs.
3 "	18.50	1.85	20 "	3 lbs.
5 "	35.50	2.30	50 "	10 lbs.

Each Filter packed in a box with full directions.

Above prices include connections for No. 1 and No. 3 Filters.

Write for discount.

New Process Liquid Carbonic Gas

New Process Liquid Carbonic Gas is put up in steel drums or cylinders containing 20 and 50 pounds of liquid gas respectively. These drums are frequently tested at a pressure of 3700 pounds to the square inch and as a further precaution against accident are provided with a safety valve which makes them absolutely safe to handle.

Price, Gas only, per pound ....$ 0.18

Price, Drums holding 20 lbs 10.00
Weight filled 100 lbs.

Price, Drums holding 50 lbs 17.50
Weight filled 130 lbs.

F. O. B.   Montreal.

Gas Drums are loaned with the understanding that they are to be promptly returned when empty, freight prepaid, in as good condition as when they were received.

If not returned within 90 days we reserve the right to make sight draft for their value as above or to charge rent for them.

When all connections are tight and Gas is used according to our directions, one pound of Liquid Carbonic Gas will charge about 10 gallons of water at 150 lbs. pressure, or will put up about 20 dozen half pints of Ginger Ale, etc., or will draw about one barrel of Beer.

Guaranteed Pure, Sweet and Odorless.

New Process Liquid Carbonic Gas.

Write for discount.

Eureka Carbonators

The Principle

The carbonating principle used in Eureka Carbonators consists in breaking the water up into the finest possible spray or mist as it enters the Carbonator, in which condition it more readily and quickly absorbs carbonic acid gas than when it is agitated.

The Operation

The operation is the same in all of our Carbonators, no matter what their size or the power by which they are operated, and is as follows :

The Water

Water is forced into the Carbonator at its highest point, where a special valve breaks it up into the finest possible spray or mist, in which condition, as it seeks the base by gravity, it is further broken up and kept in that condition by falling over pebbles of irregular size.

The Gas

Gas is admitted to the Carbonator at a point in the base from which, by a special device, it seeks the highest point, and in so doing is thoroughly absorbed by the spray of water as it descends through the pebbles.

The Power

It will be seen that this method, which makes agitation absolutely unnecessary, saves the power it would take to run an agitator. It also eliminates a large number of parts which, at times, are likely to get out of order, carbonates the water more thoroughly and faster, and saves floor space, weight, etc.

Sizes

Eureka Carbonators are made in eleven sizes and styles, and can be operated by the power most convenient to the user. They can be used by any establishment, and are fully illustrated and described on the following pages.

No. 1 Automatic Dispenser's Carbonator

Capacity 50 gallons and upwards an hour.

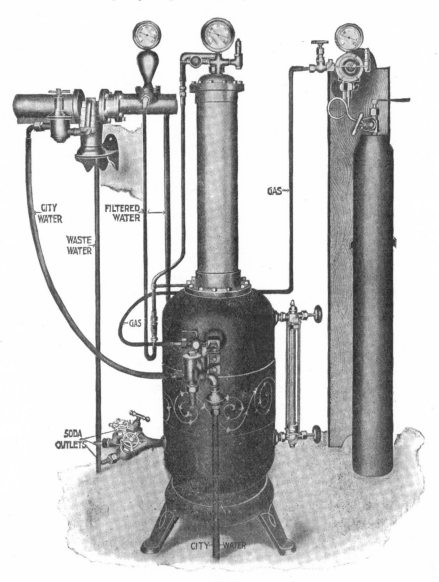

New Process Liquid Carbonic Gas

No. 1

Automatic Continuous

Dispense's Water Power Carbonator

This carbonator is absolutely automatic and continuous and is operated by a water pump which gets its power from the pressure of water in the city water pipes.

HOW OPERATED

It has a capacity of 50 gallons and upwards of perfectly carbonated water per hour, according to the city water pressure.

CAPACITY

The pump forces filtered water into the carbonator and when it reaches a certain height in the base, raises a float which closes a valve and shuts off the water supply. Whenever several gallons of soda are drawn the float drops, opens the valve, the pump starts and again fills the carbonator.

HOW IT WORKS

The carbonating principle is fully explained on page 189 and the cost of soda should not exceed 1½ cents per gallon when the apparatus is operated as we direct.

COST OF SODA

As furnished by us the apparatus consists of

1 Automatic Carbonator,	1 Water Pump,
1 No. 11 Gas Regulator,	1 Connection Gas to Carbonator,
1 Drum Board and Clamp,	1 Connection Pump to Carbonator.

Filtered water must be used to make good carbonated water.

Prices Quoted on Application.

New Process Liquid Carbonic Gas.

No. 7 Dispensers' Hand Carbonator

Capacity 40 to 50 gallons an hour.

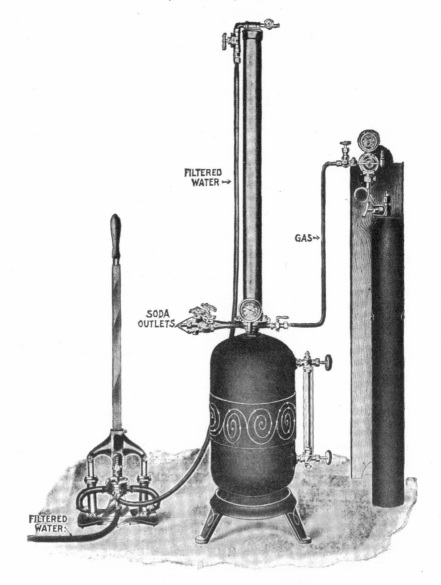

New Process Liquid Carbonic Gas.

No. 7—Dispensers' Continuous

Hand Pump Carbonator

This Carbonator is continuous in its action, and is operated by a double oscillating lever hand pump.

HOW OPERATED

The exertion required to operate is very little, it having a capacity of 40 gallons and upwards of perfectly carbonated water per hour.

CAPACITY

It will carbonate at any pressure by setting the Gas Regulator at the pressure desired, and soda should not cost over 1½ cents per gallon if our directions are followed, the carbonating principle being fully explained on page 189.

PRESSURE AND COST

As furnished by us the apparatus consists of

1 Carbonator,	1 Steel Fountain with Water Gauge,
1 No. 11 Gas Regulator,	1 Connection Gas to Carbonator,
1 Hand Pump,	1 Connection Pump to Carbonator,
1 Drum Board,	1 Spring Clamp.

For those who own their own Steel Fountains we are prepared to furnish the apparatus without the fountain, at a reduction in price, the carbonator being so made that it will fit any make of fountain, and can easily be attached by anyone. In which case it consists of

OPTION

1 Carbonator,	1 Hand Pump,
1 No. 11 Gas Regulator,	1 Set of Connections as above,
1 Drum Board,	1 Spring Clamp.

Filtered water must be used to make good carbonated water.

Prices Quoted on Application.

New Process Liquid Carbonic Gas

No. 8—Automatic Electric Carbonator

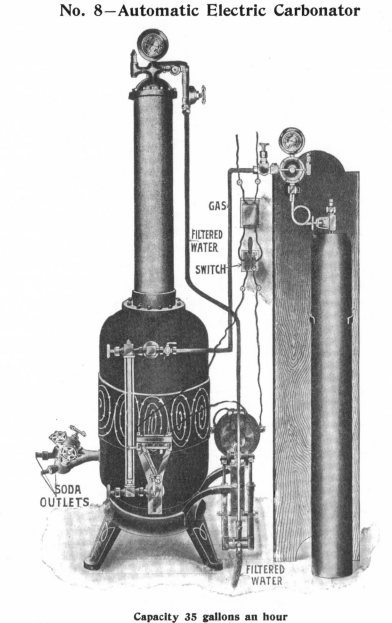

Capacity 35 gallons an hour

New Process Liquid Carbonic Gas

No. 8—Automatic Continuous

Dispensers' Electric Carbonator

This Carbonator is automatic and continuous, and is operated by an electric motor which works a duplex pump.

HOW OPERATED

It has a capacity of 40 gallons of perfectly carbonated water per hour, which will be found amply large for all but the very largest dispensers.

CAPACITY

The duplex pump forces filtered water into the carbonator, which when it reaches a certain height in the base, raises a float, which shuts off the electric current and stops the pump. Whenever several gallons of soda are drawn, the float drops. turning on the current and the pump again fills the carbonator.

HOW IT WORKS

Water can be carbonated at any pressure, by setting the Gas Regulator at the pressure wanted, and soda should not cost over 1 to 1½ cents a gallon when the apparatus is used as we direct.

PRESSURE AND COST

We furnish motors for any kind of current, but in ordering, we must be told whether it is direct or alternating and what its voltage is.

MOTORS

As furnished by us the apparatus consists of

1 Automatic Carbonator,	1 Electric Motor,
1 Gas Regulator, Board & Clamp,	1 Duplex Pump,
1 Connection Gas to Carbonator,	1 Conn. Pump to Carb.

Filtered water must be used to make good carbonated water

Prices Quoted on Application.

New Process Liquid Carbonic Gas

Bracket Carbonating Outfit

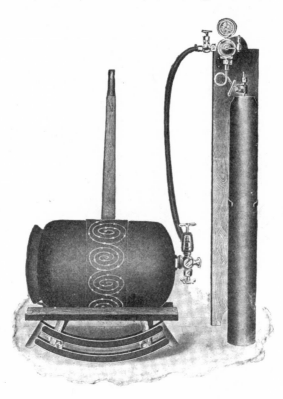

Bracket Outfit Parts

1 No. 11 H. P. Regulator,	1 Rocker,	1 Board,
1 Clamp,	1 Wall Clamp,	1 Set Hose Connections,
1 Single Connection,	8 Feet Soda Hose.	

Gas and Drums not included.

No. 1 Outfit, List Price, without Fountain...........................
No. 1 A   "   "   with   Fountain..........................

This is especially recommended for the use of druggists, confectioners and small bottling establishments. The cut shows the outfit attached to a soda fountain, ready for charging.

Gas Drums are Loaned, not Sold.

New Process Liquid Carbonic Gas

Prices Quoted on Application.

The " Ideal "

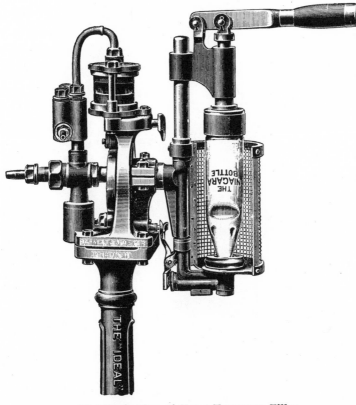

The Perfection of Hand Turnover Filler

For all Internal-Stoppered Bottles

60 to 80 dozen of first class water can be syruped and filled by a boy or a girl in one hour.

This machine will be found the Quickest, most Perfect, Reliable and Economical Machine in the Market.

Syrups, Fills, and Snifts at one operation.

It is the most rapid Filler yet introduced, and the waters produced by it are much superior to any other. It is the easiest to work, the simplest and the most lasting; having few working parts, it is not liable to get out of order, and the Syrup Pump can be altered and adjusted more quickly than in any other Turnover Filler. It has no valves in the water supply, but discs of prepared leather, which we were the first to introduce to the trade.

It effects a greater saving in Gas, Syrup, and Water than any other Machine. The average breakage of Bottles is greatly lessened by its use.

Price, each...$150.00

Write for discount.

Seltzer Water Apparatus

For Bars

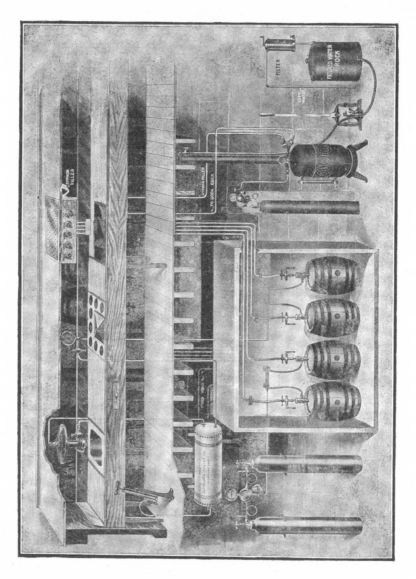

Seltzer Water Apparatus for Bars

The cut on the opposite page shows our No. 7 Continuous Hand Pump Carbonator, adapted for bar use. The use of soda and seltzer water has become so universal that our Continuous Carbonators are a great economy for bars of even only a moderately large trade, and are practically indispensable for places doing a large business.

One of our Continuous Carbonators very quickly pays for itself. After being installed practically the only cost will be for liquid carbonic acid gas, which can be bought so that the water should not cost over 2 cents per gallon, or about ½ cent per syphon, as against 8 cents per syphon or 10 cents per gallon when bought in the regular way.

A boy can run the double acting hand pump, and make from 30 to 50 gallons of perfectly carbonated water per hour.

A charging outfit for bar use, as shown on opposite page, consists of the following :

1 No. 7 Continuous Hand Pump Carbonator complete.
1 Syphon Filler and Cage.
1 No. 108A Polished Soda Faucet.
6 No. 2 Syphons.
25 ft. ⅜ in. 6 oz. B. T. Pipe for Coil.
2 12-ft. Runs 6 oz. B. T. Pipe.

Price quoted on application.

Write for catalogue of Carbonators, Electric, Hydraulic and Power.
DON'T PUT IT OFF.

You are money out every day you delay making your own Seltzer Water and filling your own Syphons.

Big and Little Wonder Pumps

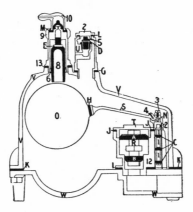

PRICE LIST OF REPAIRS

		L.W.	B.W.
A	Valve Packing, Large..	$0.20	$0.40
B	" " Small ..	0.10	0.20
C	Shift. Valve Packing, ea.	.05	.10
D	Inlet Valve Washer....	.02	.04
E	Float " "	.02	.04
F	Thomas Valve	.10	.10
G	Washer..............	.05	.10
H	"	.02	.04
I	Valve Gasket	.25	.50
J	Washer..............	.10	.20
K	Body Gasket..........	.55	1.10
L	Washer..............	.05	.10
M	"	.05	.10
N	Float Lever Pin	.10	.20
O	Float Ball............	3.60	5.00
P	Inlet Valve complete...	2.20	4.40
R	Main Valve complete...	1.75	3.50
	Complete Set Packings.	.80	1.50

		L.W.	B.W.
S	Float Lever, complete.	$0.70	$1.40
T	Valve Cap	.55	1.10
V	Shell	7.70	14.00
W	Base	4.15	8.00
1	Valve complete.......	1.35	2.50
2	Inlet Valve Cap	.40	.80
2-3-4	Screws, dozen....	.25	.35
5	Rubber Valve	.15	.30
6	Screw for Float	.45	.75
8	Outlet Float..........	.25	.50
9	Swivel Nut...........	.35	.70
10	Swivel	.45	.90
12	Main Valve Casing ...	6.00	10.00
	Outlet " complete..	2.50	4.00
13	Rubber Washer	.03	.05
	Brass Cap Screws....	.10	.15
	Roller and Pin........	.15	.25

New Process Liquid Carbonic Gas

Write for discount.

The Champion Automatic Vacuum Ale Lift

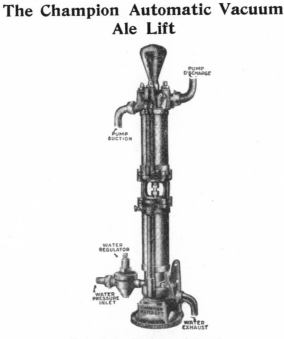

Patented. Name registered

This Lift operates by water pressure, automatically, drawing the ale from the barrel by *suction* and imparting a slight pressure in delivering it to the faucet. This pressure can be so regulated as to draw the ale flat or with a fine bead, as desired.

It is absolutely reliable, and stands on a par with our Celebrated Hydraulic Beer Pumps. It is past the experimental stage, and is revolutionizing the old method of drawing ale by hand.

Its essential features are : Smooth action, even stroke, regulated pressure, tin lined cylinders. Requires no attention. Easy to repack. It stands 31 in. high. Weighs 29 lbs.

List price, including pressure regulator and couplings...........$69.50

Made in different sizes to suit conditions of water pressure and pumping elevation, which should always be specified when ordering. Further particulars furnished on application.

No. 1—Ale Strainer

This strainer is to connect with suction on Ale Lift to keep out loose hops.

Tinned throughout. Strainer easily removed and cleaned.

List price........$ 3.50

Satisfaction guaranteed

Write for discount.

Crown Cork Soda Machine
(New Automatic)

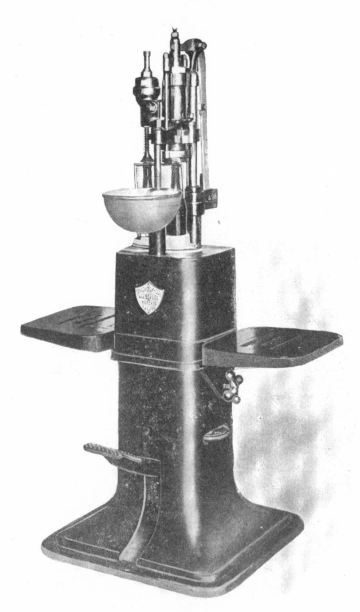

For filling and crowning Aerated Waters. Strong and durable. Rapid, easy and effective in operation. Full directions accompany each machine.

Price on application.

Crown Cork Beer Machine

(Steam Power)

For Crowning Beers, Ale, Wine, etc. Recommended for use in large breweries. Full directions accompany each machine. Price on application.

Crown Cork Beer Machine
(Foot Power)

For Crowning Beers, Ales, Wines, etc. Full directions accompany each machine.   Price on application.

No. 39—" Corkee " with Clamp
Corking Machine

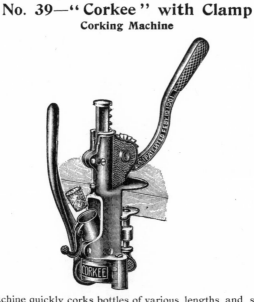

This machine quickly corks bottles of various lengths and sizes. It will cork two bottles while corking one with other makes. The Cork can be driven into bottles any distance required. To drive a cork a less distance, raise the adjusting rod, which can be held at any height by means of the set screw. Corks should always be softened in hot water (not used dry). This article supplies a long felt want.

Nickel-plated, each $11.00
Black Japan Finish, each 9.00

Combination Lid Holder

25¢ *Straight*

And Price Card for Cigar Boxes

Price, per hundred ....$ 6.00
"   " thousand 54.00

Write for discount.

Bar Fixture No. 410—" The Imperial "

Bar Fixture No. 410—" The Imperial "

My new design for the new century ; artistic, massive and attractive.   A complete fixture, costly in design and of the best workmanship and finish.   The heavy cornice with carved panels, supported by massive pillars, gives the entire outfit an appearance of grandeur and stability.   Made in Oak or Birch, all colors.

Counter—Massive and subtantial, with carved pilasters supporting top, solid rail and beer gutter on rear side.   Hard oil finish.   Mahogany top.   Height, 43 inches ; width, 20 inches.

Back Bar—With glass doors and ice-box.

Mirror Frame—Heavy carved cornice, supported by massive square carved and fluted pillars, fitted with three British plate bevelled mirrors.   Height of frame, 72 inches.

Total height of fitting, 10 ft.

No. 410, Oak or Birch, as above, 10 ft. mirrors, 40 x 60 and 40 x 18 . . . .$350.00

No. 410, Oak or Birch, as above, 15 ft. mirrors, 40 x 72 and 40 x 24 . . . .$525.00

No. 410, Oak or Birch, as above, 20 ft. mirrors, 40 x 100 and 40 x 36 . . . .$700.00

Special prices on application for other lengths.

Drawings and estimates for special designs furnished on application.

Write for discount.

Bar Fixture, No. 400—" THE I. X. L. "

Bar Fixture No. 400—" The I. X. L. "

A modern bar fixture of latest design ; a complete moderate-priced outfit, consisting of counter, back bar and mirror frame. Made in oak or birch, highly finished.

Counter—Strongly made, with pilasters and panelled front, solid arm rail and beer gutter on inner side. Mahogany top, highly finished, hard oil rubbed. Height, 43 inches ; width, 20 inches ; any length.

Back Bar—With panel doors.

Mirror Frame—Has heavy cornice, with hand carving supported by square pilaster ; shelves at each end and fitted with British plate bevelled mirror, in 10 ft. case, 36 x 60 inches. Height, 60 inches. Total height, 9 ft.

The whole forming an up-to-date bar, at a moderate cost.

" The I. X. L. Bar Fixture, complete, as described above :

10 feet long, for.................................$250.00
15 feet long, for 375.00
20 feet long, for.................................. 500.00

Special price, on application for larger sizes.

Drawings and estimates for special designs furnished on application.

WORK BOARDS

Complete Under Counter Arrangement of Style "D" Work Board Ends and No. 73 Combination Box

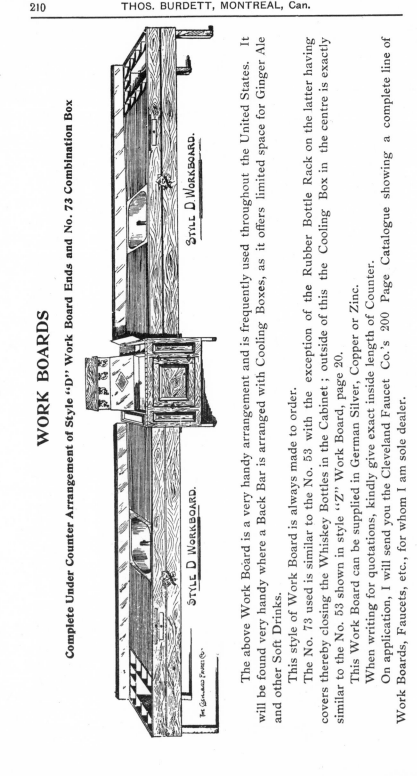

The above Work Board is a very handy arrangement and is frequently used throughout the United States. It will be found very handy where a Back Bar is arranged with Cooling Boxes, as it offers limited space for Ginger Ale and other Soft Drinks.

This style of Work Board is always made to order.

The No. 73 used is similar to the No. 53 with the exception of the Rubber Bottle Rack on the latter having covers thereby closing the Whiskey Bottles in the Cabinet; outside of this the Cooling Box in the centre is exactly similar to the No. 53 shown in style "Z" Work Board, page 20.

This Work Board can be supplied in German Silver, Copper or Zinc.

When writing for quotations, kindly give exact inside length of Counter.

On application, I will send you the Cleveland Faucet Co.'s 200 Page Catalogue showing a complete line of Work Boards, Faucets, etc., for whom I am sole dealer.

Work Boards—*Continued*

Complete Under Counter Arrangement of No. 62 Box and Style "H" Work Board Ends

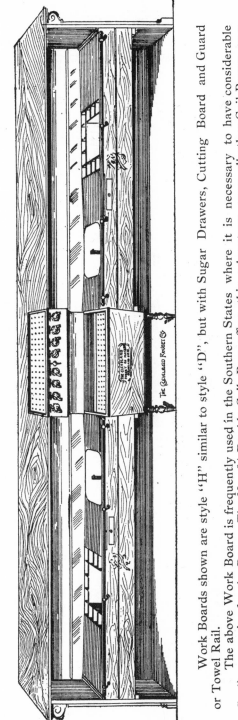

Work Boards shown are style "H" similar to style "D", but with Sugar Drawers, Cutting Board and Guard and Guard or Towel Rail.

The above Work Board is frequently used in the Southern States where it is necessary to have considerable Cooling capacity for the Beer. The No. 64 Double Coil Box offers this advantage over all other Coil Boxes, as a considerable amount of Pipe can be placed in the lower or upper section of the Coil Box, or the upper or lower part can be used separately.

This Work Board can ce supplied in German Silver, Copper or Zinc.

When writing for quotations, kindly give exact inside length of counter.

On application, I will send you the Cleveland Faucet Co's 200 Page Catalogue showing a complete line of Work Boards, Faucets, etc., for whom I am sole dealer.

Work Boards—*Continued*

Complete Under Counter Arrangement of Style "K" Work Board with one No. 93 Combination Box and one No. 174 Cooler at each end

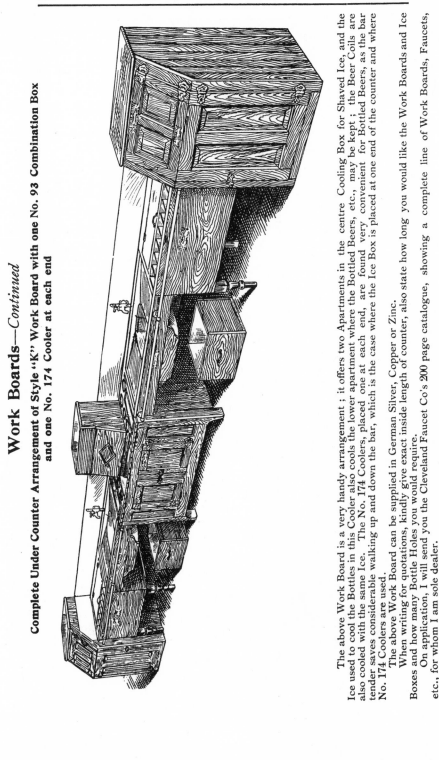

The above Work Board is a very handy arrangement ; it offers two Apartments in the centre Cooling Box for Shaved Ice, and the Ice used to cool the Bottles in this Cooler also cools the lower apartment where the Bottled Beers, etc., may be kept ; the Beer Coils are also cooled with the same Ice. The No. 174 Coolers, placed one at each end, are found very convenient for Bottled Beers, as the bar tender saves considerable walking up and down the bar, which is the case where the Ice Box is placed at one end of the counter and where No. 174 Coolers are used.

The above Work Board can be supplied in German Silver, Copper or Zinc.

When writing for quotations, kindly give exact inside length of counter, also state how long you would like the Work Boards and Ice Boxes and how many Bottle Holes you would require.

On application, I will send you the Cleveland Faucet Co's 200 page catalogue, showing a complete line of Work Boards, Faucets, etc., for whom I am sole dealer.

Work Boards—*Continued*

Complete Under Counter Arrangement Style "W" Work Board with No. 111 Coil Box and No. 174 Coolers placed at each End

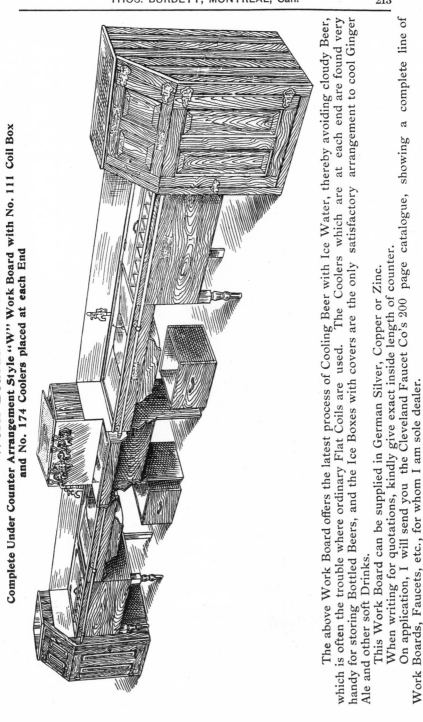

The above Work Board offers the latest process of Cooling Beer with Ice Water, thereby avoiding cloudy Beer, which is often the trouble where ordinary Flat Coils are used. The Coolers which are at each end and are found very handy for storing Bottled Beers, and the Ice Boxes with covers are the only satisfactory arrangement to cool Ginger Ale and other soft Drinks.

This Work Board can be supplied in German Silver, Copper or Zinc.

When writing for quotations, kindly give exact inside length of counter.

On application, I will send you the Cleveland Faucet Co's 200 page catalogue, showing a complete line of Work Boards, Faucets, etc., for whom I am sole dealer.

Work Boards—*Continued*

Complete Under Counter Arrangement of Style "X" Work Board and three Cooling Boxes with Covers and Bottle Racks.

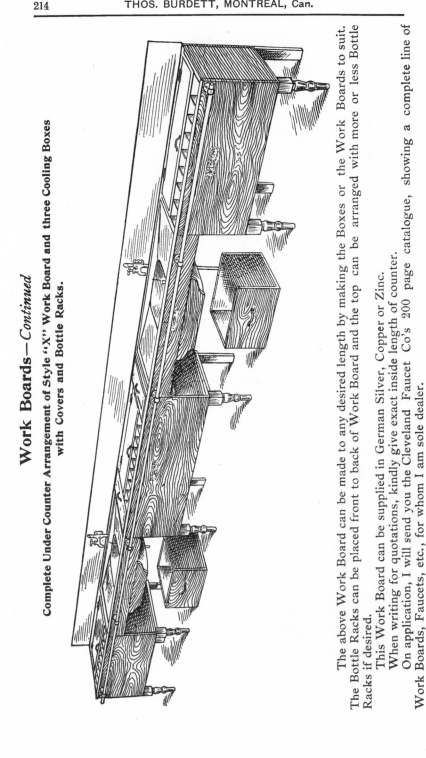

The above Work Board can be made to any desired length by making the Boxes or the Work Boards to suit. The Bottle Racks can be placed front to back of Work Board and the top can be arranged with more or less Bottle Racks if desired.

This Work Board can be supplied in German Silver, Copper or Zinc.

When writing for quotations, kindly give exact inside length of counter.

On application, I will send you the Cleveland Faucet Co's 200 page catalogue, showing a complete line of Work Boards, Faucets, etc., for whom I am sole dealer.

Work Boards—*Continued*

Complete Under Counter Arrangement of *Style "Z"* Work Board with a No. 53 Combination Box in the centre and one No. 34 Cooler at each End.

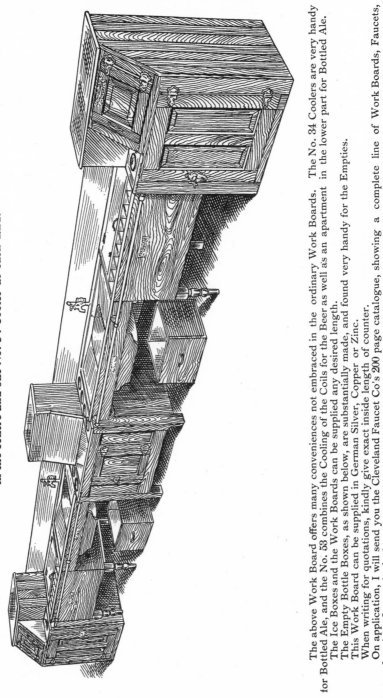

The above Work Board offers many conveniences not embraced in the ordinary Work Boards. The No. 34 Coolers are very handy for Bottled Ale, and the No. 53 combines the Cooling of the Coils for the Beer as well as an apartment in the lower part for Bottled Ale.

The Ice Boxes and the Work Boards can be supplied any desired length.

The Empty Bottle Boxes, as shown below, are substantially made, and found very handy for the Empties.

This Work Board can be supplied in German Silver, Copper or Zinc.

When writing for quotations, kindly give exact inside length of counter.

On application, I will send you the Cleveland Faucet Co's 200 page catalogue, showing a complete line of Work Boards, Faucets, etc., for whom I am sole dealer.

The Madison

Here we illustrate another one of our latest designs. In its beauty, massiveness and veneered construction, it has no equal. We wish to call special attention to the artistic carved caps and lion heads which are a piece of art and together with the graceful outlines, are always admired by all. The counter is made of a rich O. G. pattern, fitted with a genuine mahogany top, improved roll arm rail, and mixing board or gutter. For finish and length, see right hand corner. For further information see price list.

Lengths 18, 20 and 24 feet.

Curley Birch, finished Mahogany or Quarter Sawed Oak, Golden Oak Finish.

Fixture Height, 11 feet, 0 inches.

To Buyers of Saloon Fixtures

The wood used in the construction of our fixtures is first thoroughly seasoned by atmospheric exposure, kiln dried after the most improved methods. This is a guarantee of any of our goods shrinking or cracking, which is the general complaint about goods made in the old way, or by manufacturers who have not the necessary way or means to season their material.

Write for our illustrative and descriptive catalogue.

Prices on application.

Thos. Burdett, Sole agent for Canada for Chas. Passow & Sons, Chicago, Ill. Largest Bar Fixture Manufacturers in the world.

The Taylor

Here we have a set of fixtures that is fit for a palace. The mirror frame has two turned columns; above these columns is a heavy cornice which with its hand carved ornaments and mouldings make a costly appearance. The counter is made to harmonize with the balance of the fixtures and has neat panels and pilasters ; the counter top is fitted with a patent roll arm rail and wood beer gutter or mixing board. For further information see Price List.

Lengths, sizes 14 and 16 feet.

Select Oak, Golden Finish, Select Birch, Mahogany Finish.

Height, 9 feet 6 inches.

Do you know Champion of Billiard FRANK IVES broke the World's Billiard Record on our table.

Do you know what the press said about the record made on Chas. Passow & Sons Billiard and Pool Tables.

Write for Catalogue. Prices on application.

Thomas Burdett, Sole Agent for Canada for Chas. Passow & Sons, Chicago, Ill. Largest Bar Fixture Manufacturers in the world.

The Washington

This style is especially designed for those wishing something extra fine and rich in appearance ; it surpasses all other fixtures in beauty and elegance. The mirror frame has four heavy columns with elaborately carved caps, the arches are richly decorated with lion heads brought out in bold relief.   The corners and flat surfaces between the arches are surmounted with large carved shields which add to the beauty of this outfit.   The counter is made of rich O. G. pattern, the top is made of genuine mahogany, fitted with roll rail and wood mixing board or gutter. For further information see price list.

Lengths, 24 and 30 feet.

Quarter Sawed Oak, Golden Curley Birch, Mahogany finish.

Height, 11 feet 6 inches.

Reasons why we can sell Cheaper than all Others.

FIRST REASON :—Our factories are in a lumber district and buy our lumber in large lots, saving us 25 per cent. on our lumber.

SECOND REASON :—We own and operate our factory, warehouses and salesrooms, which you see on cover of this catalogue, saving 50 per cent. over others who have to pay rent.

Prices on application.

Thomas Burdett, Sole Agent for Canada for Chas. Passow & Sons, Chicago, Ill. Largest Bar Manufacturers in the world.

The Adams

In the above design we illustrate the partition, liquor case, cigar case and wainscoting which harmonizes with the design on the opposite page. The partition is shown with bevel cut and chipped plate glass set in metallic sash, oxidized copper finish, but can be fitted with Colonial glass or French plate mirrors. The swing doors are hung on double acting cold rolled steel spring hinges. The cigar case is built as light as possible in consistency with a substantial construction, and has a bevel plate glass top and double thick glass in front and sides and provided with suitable moistening trays. Liquor case arranged in lower section with cupboards and in upper section with adjustable shelves and doors fitted with double strength glass. Liquor case and Cigar case carried in stock : 4, 5 and 6 ft. long. For further information see price list.

Notice, Saloonkeepers

You receive the same treatment by mail as if you were here in person, and we know there is no concern in Canada that can compete with us in quality and price.

Write for our large illustrated and *Descriptive Catalogue of Saloon Fixtures.*

You will save at least 25 per cent, if you get our prices before ordering any goods in our line.

Prices on application.

Thomas Burdett, sole agent for Canada for Chas. Passow & Sons, Chicago, Ill. Largest Bar Fixture Manufacturers in the world.

The Economy

This Outfit consists of solid oak Counter, Back Bar, Mirror, Work Bar,
Foot Rail.   Finished the latest style dark English finish.

A complete 12 ft. Solid Oak Outfit.

The above is a sample of our low prices.

Mirrors are made of best quality French Polished Plate.

Work Bar is lined with the very best Zinc.

The Foot Rail is made of Iron and has patent Lift Brackets.

Prices on application.

Thomas Burdett, sole agent for Canada for Chas. Passow & Sons, Chicago,
Ill.   Largest Bar Fixture Manufacturers in the world.

Portable Electric Hand Lamp

Always ready to illuminate any dark places.
Every Bar Room, Hotel and Saloon should have one.
No danger when in contact with any explosive material.
Battery will last three to four months.

Price, each...$ 5.00
Renewal Batteries, each .... .50

Electric Pocket Lamp

A very handy article.   Always ready.
No danger when in contact with any explosive material.
Battery will last three to four months.

Price, each...$ 3.00
Renewal Batteries, each... .50

Electric Gas Lighter

Price, each ....$ 3.00
Renewal Batteries, each...................................... .50

Write for discount.

No. 45—Hawthorne Julep Strainer

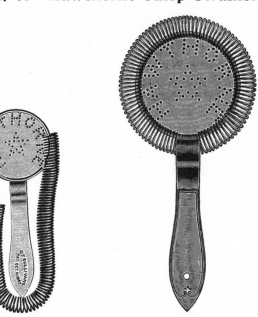

The best in the world.

The adjustable Wire Coil can be removed or replaced at will. This great advantage (for cleaning), over any other wire strainer, will be readily seen.

Silver-plated, per dozen......................................$15.50

To avoid corrosion the parts of the "Gem Spoon" coming in contact with the cream, are made from non-corrosive metal, and finished in the best Triple Silver-plate.

Carried in stock in the following sizes :

6, 8, 10, 12, 16 and 20 to the quart.

Price, each..$ 3.00

Write for discount.

Mathon Wood Faucet

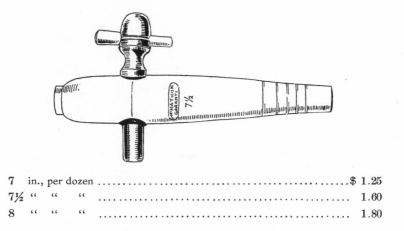

7   in., per dozen ....$ 1.25

7½ "   "   " 1.60

8   "   "   " 1.80

No. 348--Metal Faucets

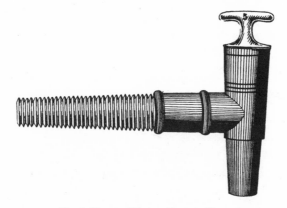

Best Heavy Tin.   Screw Key

No. 1, per dozen ....$ 2.60

    2, "   " 3.25

    3, "   " 4.25

    4, "   " 5.00

    5, "   " 6.00

    6, "   " 7.00

Write for discount.

**No. N 1016
Combination
Plant
36 in. high**

A pretty window plant, made up of a number of natural prepared palm and areca leaves, all removable. This makes a nice combination and a plant which is exceptionally fine value for the money.

Price, each, without pot..................................... $3.00

Wine and Whiskey Felt Filtering Bag

E 20	¼ gal., each	....	$1.35
E 21	½ "	....	1.60
E 22	1 "	....	1.95
E 23	2 "	....	3.10
E 24	3 "	....	4.15

A Felt Filtering Bag is as necessary to the conduct of a well regulated saloon or liquor house as are the goods themselves.

Write for discount.

Georgia Palm Plant

This plant is an exact imitation of the growing Southern palm, and may be had in almost any height or number of leaves desired. Exceptionally good value.

No. N 1005 with 5 leaves, 24 in. high, price, each................ $1.50

No. N 1006 " 5 " 36 "   " 1.70

No. N 1007 " 6 " 42 "   " 2.25

Our Palms are all the genuine Southern plants, with the leaves scientifically treated so that they lastingly retain their color and shape. The stems of the leaves are flexible and can be bent to any desired shape and will then stay that way. These palms are all exceptionally fine and make a great display.

Prices above quoted do not include pots.

Write for discount.   15

Our Grand Bouquet

No. N 1098—Without pot, 40 inches high.   Made up of 6 velvet Begonia leaves and an assortment of full-blown flowers, consisting of American Beauty Roses, Rose Buds, Lilacs and Lilies, making beyond question the handsomest, most bushy and elaborate appearing plants that human hands have been capable of making.

Price, each..$17.00

No. N 1099—Without pot.   Same as above but smaller.

Price, each 9.00

Write for discount.

Novelty Back Bar Decanters

No. E 4050	No. E 4051
Before Taking	**After Taking**

A comical etched glass decanter or bar bottle, with glass stopper, showing dissatisfied man with an expression indicating that he craves a drink.

Never happier in his life, an etched bottle or decanter which makes a good back bar ornament and pleasing bottle from which to take a drink.

Price, each $0.75

Price, each $0.75

Write for discount.

No. 1729 — Imitation Cut Glass Straw Jar

No. 1728 — Square Pressed Straw Jar

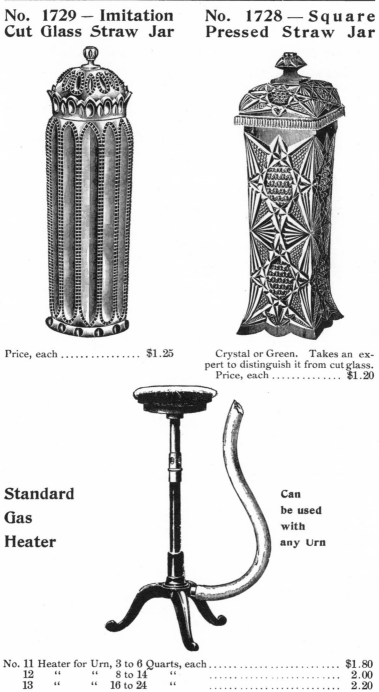

Price, each $1.25

Crystal or Green. Takes an expert to distinguish it from cut glass.
Price, each $1.20

Standard

Gas

Heater

Can be used with any Urn

No. 11 Heater for Urn, 3 to 6 Quarts, each......................... $1.80
    12   "   " 8 to 14 " 2.00
    13   "   " 16 to 24 " 2.20

Write for discount.

Sample Bottle-Squat.

Also used as odd shape bottle frequently for bar use.

Glass Graduate

Engraved numbers.

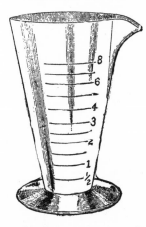

No. E 65, 6 oz., per doz.... $1.80
   E 66, 8 "   " 2.00
   E 67, 12 "   " 2.25
   E 68, 16 "   " 2.70

No. E 14- 2 oz., each....... $0.35
   E 15- 4   " 0.50
   E 16- 8   " 0.70
   E 17-16   " 1.00
   E 18-32   " 1.95

No. E 40

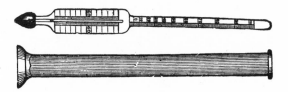

Hydrometer and Jar for determining proof strength of spirits, whiskey, etc. Ordinary business care requires every liquor dealer to test his goods carefully, both on receiving same and before re-shipping. This instrument will do the work perfectly. Used by U. S. Custom House.

Price, complete with full instructions............................ $3.75
Jar only 1.35
Hydrometer only.. 2.50

Write for discount.

The Icecubator

A perfect Ice Cutting Machine

Economy, cleanliness, individuality and a high grade service in ice is guaranteed where this machine is used. It will more than pay for itself in one season, and it is indispensable for Hotel and Restaurant use, and very desirable for making hi-balls and other like drinks.

Weighs 200 lbs., is built entirely of iron and steel.

It produces Cubes or Diamond shapes in five sizes: 1, 1¼, 1½, 1¾ and 2 inches.

Price, each $275.00
Write for discount.

No. D 315 — Windsor Hi Ball Ice Tongs

7¾ inch. long. The highest grade article of its kind made.

Extra heavy silver plated on solid nickel. Will last a life time.

Price, each $4.60

Heavy Steel Ice Tongs

No. D 2521, Opens, 12 inches ....$ 2.40
    D 2522,   "   14 inches 3.00
    D 2523,   "   17 inches 3.50
    D 2524,   "   24 inches 4.25

Just the kind that are used in hotels, restaurants and saloons.

Write for discount.

Combination Cork Press and Capping Machine

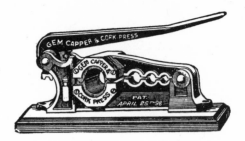

This Machine is strongly built

Will press any size cork and press the tin foil caps onto bottles perfectly.
Price, each $12.00

No. D 32—Cork Press

This unique cork press will press corks of all sizes to fit bottles or flasks.
Made of iron, black enameled.
Price, each $0.85

No. D 161—Leg Pocket Cork Puller

Showing legs with enameled striped stockings.   Very novel.
Price, each.. $1.70

Write for discount.

Round Papier Mache Trays

These Trays possess the three qualities which are very essential, neat, serviceable and light weight.

No. D 3542 8 inch, doz $6.00
No. D 3543 10 "   " 7.20
No. D 3544 12 "   " 9.20
No. D 3545 14 "   " 12.00

Square Papier Mache Trays

These Trays possess the three qualities which are very essential. Neat, serviceable and light weight. Black with gold stars. Square style, like cut.

No. D 3534 6 inch, doz $3.50
No. D 3535 8 "   " 5.40
No. D 3536 10 "   " 6.00
No. D 3537 12 "   " 9.00
No. D 3538 14 "   " 12.00
No. D 3539 16 "   " 15.50
No. D 3540 20 "   " 25.00
No. D 3541 24 "   " 37.00

Oval Japanned Tray

No. D 3512 12 inch, doz $3.00
No. D 3513 14 "   " 3.50
No. D 3514 16 "   " 4.00
No. D 3515 18 "   " 5.20
No. D 3516 20 "   " 6.00
No. D 3517 22 "   " 8.00
No. D 3518 24 "   " 9.00
No. D 3519 26 "   " 12.00
No. D 3520 28 "   " 16.00

Write for discount.

Hotel or Confectioners'

(With Fly Wheel)

This machine is designed especially for hotels, cafes and ice cream parlors. It is the regular hand freezer, with flywheel substituted in place of crank. Other power should never be used. It has the celebrated duplex dasher with single self-adjusting wood scraping bar.

No. .... V 120
Quarts 12
Each......$26.00

No. .... V 121
Quarts 15
Each......$34.00

No. .... V 122
Quarts 20
Each......$42.00

No. .... V 123
Quarts 25
Each......$52.00

Improved White Mountain

A very important and exclusive feature of the White Mountain Freezer is its duplex malleable iron dasher, being made in two parts entirely distinct and independent of each other in their operation.

From the construction of this Double Beater the White Mountain Freezer derives its triple motion.

A strong water-proof tub, bound with heavy galvanized iron hoops ; the gearing is completely covered ; cans made of the very best quality of tinplate ; beaters of malleable iron and tinned ; all castings attached to tub nicely galvanized, to prevent rusting.

Nos	V 126	V 127	V 128	V 129
Quarts...................	4	6	8	10
Each	$7.25	$10.50	$13.00	$17.00
Nos	V 130	V 131	V 132	V 133
Quarts...................	12	15	20	25
Each	$21.50	$25.50	$33.00	$42.00

Write for discount.

No. 5171—Fancy Bar Coat

No. 5172—Fancy Bar Coat

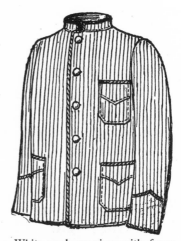

White corduroy pique, first water white pearl buttons, with white silk cord binding on edges, cuffs and pockets; lay down collar.

Price, each $4.60

White corduroy pique with fancy white silk cord binding on edges, cuffs and collars. Standup military collar and first water pearl buttons

Price, each $4.60

No. 5173—Swell Bar Coat

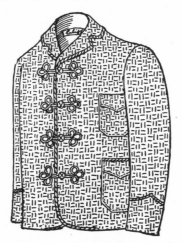

Fancy basket weave duck. Silk cord binding on edges, cuffs and pockets; silkoline loops.

Price, each.. $4.75

The garments illustrated above are made in the latest style with the Nobby Effect of Silk Cord Binding.

This gives a very swell appearance and will make the above line one of the most popular ever designed.

Write for discount.

No. 1038   Dice Top

Made of selected bone. Size of top varying from 1 inch to 1½ inch, and is numbered from 1 to 8. Is made to spin high or low, as wanted, and is easily manupulated. A novelty which will afford considerable amusement.
Price, each............... .... $1.70

DICE BOXES

No. S 1045—Leather Dice Box

Extra well made ; hand sewed ; best quality tan leather.
Size 2⅝ inches diameter, 36 inches high.
Price, each $0.60

No. S 1046

Size 2¾ inches diameter, 3¾ inches high.
Price, each $1.00

No. S 1047—Imitation Ivory Dice Box

Made of one piece of patent ivory, perfectly smooth on inside. Bottom lined with velvet. Handsomest and best box made.

Price, each.............. $1.45

No. D 224   Sink Cleaner

Sheet metal pan to gather waste substance with brush on edge for cleaning corners, nitches, etc.
Each... $0.25

Write for discount.

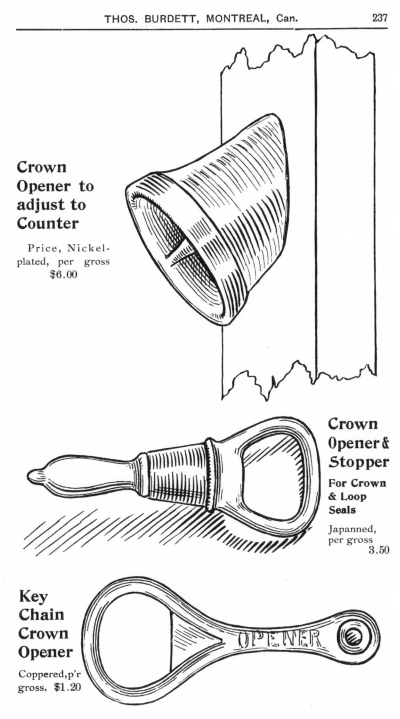

Crown Opener to adjust to Counter

Price, Nickel-plated, per gross $6.00

Crown Opener & Stopper

For Crown & Loop Seals

Japanned, per gross 3.50

Key Chain Crown Opener

Coppered, p'r gross. $1.20

OPENER

Write for discount.

The "Century" Cash Register

A total adder. The Lowest Priced Total Adding Cash Register on the market. Solid metal case handsomely finished in nickel or antique copper. 31 keys, including "paid out", "received on account" and "charge" keys. Pressing on one key records sale, displays amount to customer, rings bell and opens money drawer. We absolutely guarantee this register for five years ; ordinary care in handling it will preserve it for an ordinary business lifetime. This Register is absolutely accurate and cannot be cheated in any way. Whatever sum is displayed as registered will be added into the total sales. as this machine will add up to $1,000,000 it does not have to be turned back every day, but can be allowed to run indefinitely.

Price for Complete Guaranteed Register.......................... $130.00

Write for discount.

Card, Ice Cream and Lunch Tables

Light, Cleanly, Artistic, Sanitary, Attractive, Comfortable, Inexpensive and Indestructible

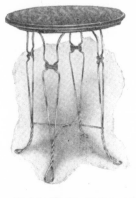

Frame—Japanese Copper Finish, Highly Polished Top, Quarter-sawed Oak or Birch.

No. 301 M, 24 in. diameter, Oak $11.50	Birch............ ....$10.00
303 M, 30 " " 13.00	" 11.50
305 M, 36 " " 14.50	" 13.00
307 M, 42 " " 16.50	" 14.50

No. 3 M—Chair

SODA COUNTER STOOLS

No. 237 M—Steel

Quartered Oak or Mahogany Seat, Frame Steel, Japanese Copper Finish, Highly Polished.	24 inches high. 12 inch. diameter Seat. Made any length up to 30 inches.
Price.................... $6.25	Price, each $5.25

Write for discount.

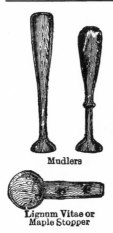

Mudlers

Lignum Vitæ or
Maple Stopper

Lignum Vitæ Stoppers, per dozen ....$ 1.90
Maple Stoppers, per dozen.................... 0.95

6 inch. Maple Muddler, per dozen $0.95
6 inch. Lignum Vitæ Muddler, per dozen.......................... 5.50
8 inch. Maple Muddler, per dozen 1.40
8 inch. Lignum Vitæ Muddler, per dozen.......................... 6.50
10 inch. Maple Muddler, per dozen 2.20
10 inch. Lignum Vitæ Muddler, per dozen......................... 7.00

Bung Starters

The Best Hickory Bung Starters Made

Flat Handle, Mortized, each ....$ 0.60
Flat Handle, Dovetailed, Riveted, each.... .... 0.80
Flat Handle, Centre Bore not Riveted, each...................... 1.00
Flat Handle, Centre Bore Riveted, each 1.20

Wooden Beer Vents

Price, per dozen ....$ 5.00

Write for discount.

Aluminum Lemon Squeezer

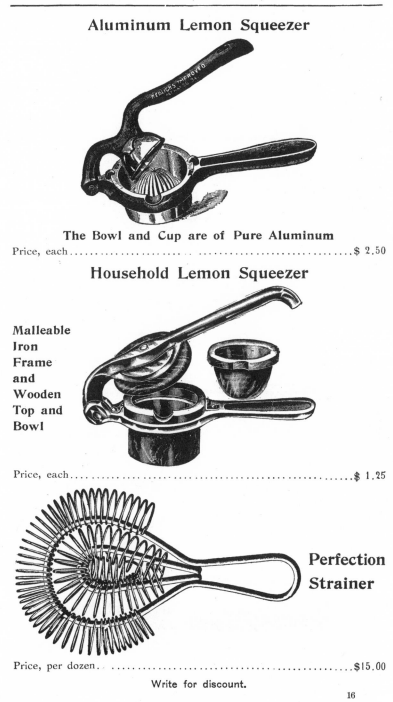

The Bowl and Cup are of Pure Aluminum

Price, each...$ 2.50

Household Lemon Squeezer

**Malleable
Iron
Frame
and
Wooden
Top and
Bowl**

Price, each...$ 1.25

Perfection
Strainer

Price, per dozen. $15.00

Write for discount.

16

Outfit No 26
Fairbanks-Morse Vertical Engine, Belted to Fairbanks-Morse Dynamo

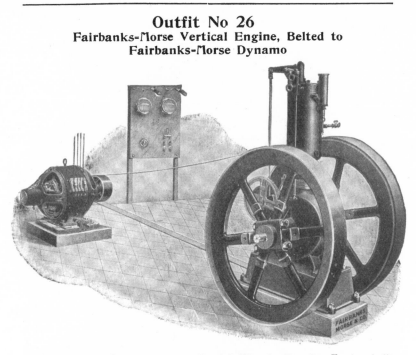

The above outfit represents our Special Electric Gasoline Engine, built with extra heavy fly wheels, belted to a Fairbanks-Morse dynamo, and will give a good, steady light ; it is also used for charging plants, charging storage batteries for automobiles. If arc lights are desired, figure on the proportion of 1 to 10 as compared with 16 c. p. lights.

Outfits of this kind are rapidly being put in for small lighting plants in country residences, where the engine can be used during the day to supply water for sprinkling lawns and furnishing a supply for water system ; with proper pump it will supply from 300 to 3,000 gallons per hour, depending on size of engine and conditions of water supply. The belt and switchboard are not included in the outfit.

With Slow Speed Dynamo

H.P.	Engine Speed	BELT FLY WHEELS		Capacity in 16 C.P. Lamps	Weight Complete	Floor Sp'ce Feet	DYNAMO		
		Diam.	Face				No. of Frame	Approx. Speed	Type
2	400	28"	3¼"	20	1,135	9 x 2	5 / 0	1,790	E
6	350	42"	4¼"	60	2,700	13 x 3	3 / 0	1,400	E

With Moderate Speed Dynamos

3	350	36"	3¼"	30	1,610	11 x 2'2"	5 / 0	1,850	E
4	350	36"	3¼"	40	2,110	9 x 2	5 / 0	1,850	E
6	350	42"	4¼"	60	2,540	10 x 2	4 / 0	1,750	E

Better Lighted than from Public Lights

RUSSELLVILLE, ARK., Oct. 3, 1902.

For two years I have been using a 2 H. P. Fairbanks-Morse Gasoline Engine to run a dynamo that makes twenty lights, and have found that it gives perfect satisfaction ; in fact, my store is better lighted than the stores using the public lights.

Yours truly,

R. J. WILSON.

Price on application.

Outfit No 12
The 2, 3, 4 and 6 H. P. Vertical Engine

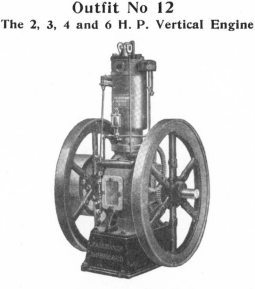

This cut represents our Vertical Gasoline Engine mounted on an iron base. It is strong and substantial and adapted for general power where an engine is required furnished with gasoline tank located outside of the building and water supply at a convenient point. This engine is also supplied with exhaust pot and pipe. (See accessories). Can furnish either salammoniac or dry battery, as preferred.

Specifications and Sizes

H. P.	Floor Space	Pulley on Engine Shaft		Speed of Engine	Shipping Weight	Export Shipping Weight
2	24" x 24½"	8 x 4		400	670	700
3	28" x 28"	10 x 5	Single	350	1200	1025
4	28" x 30"	12 x 6	Belt	350	1500	1355
6	36" x 38"	16 x 8		350	2000	1720

For export shipment these engines are supplied without cooling or gasoline tanks or their pipe and fittings, as in most cases these can be readily obtained at point of installation, effecting a considerable saving in freight charges. It will, therefore, be understood that the export shipping weights given above do not include the tanks, pipe and fittings.

Accessories

With each Vertical Gasoline Engine on iron base, as shown above, we furnish when desired :
One Pulley, standard size. (See list above).
One Electric Battery and spark coil.
One galvanized steel Gasoline Supply Tank, with two lengths of pipe and fittings to connect tank to engine.
One galvanized steel Cooling Tank, with pipe and fittings to connect to engine.
One Burner Tank for gasoline which heats tube, with two lengths of pipe and fittings to connect to engine.
One Exhaust Pot and one length Exhaust Pipe.
Twelve Ignition Tubes, necessary Wrenches and Oil Can.

Price on application.

Outfit No 1

The Jack-of-All Trades Engine, also the 3 H. P. and 4 H. P.

This illustration represents the Jack-of-All Trades without pump attachment, mounted on wood base and self-contained, having gasoline and cooling tank, all complete and connected to the engine.

The 3 and 4 horse-power engines mounted this way are much lighter than with the iron base mounting, and being self-contained, can be conveniently moved from place to place.

Order by Horse Power and Outfit Number

Specifications and Sizes

H. P.	Floor Space	Pulley on Engine Shaft	Speed of Engine	Shipping Weight
2	48" x 27"	8" x 4"	400	670
3	60" x 27"	10" x 5"	350	1055
4	60" x 28½"	12" x 6"	350	1250

Price on application.

Cedar Faucets

Without Lining

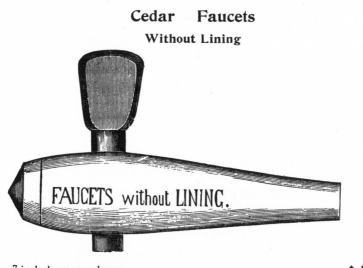

```
7 inch. long, per dozen ............................................$ 1.60
8 inch. long, per dozen ............................................  1.90
9 inch. long, per dozen ............................................  2.30
10 inch. long, per dozen ...........................................  2.80
```

Redlich's Warranted Faucets

Cork Lined. Fully Saturated with India Rubber

```
No.  1,  7    inch. long, per dozen.................................$ 1.25
     2,  8    inch. long, per dozen.................................  1.60
     3,  8½   inch. long, per dozen.................................  1.90
     4,  9½   inch. long, per dozen.................................  2.20
     5, 10½   inch. long, per dozen.................................  2.50
     6, 11½   inch. long, per dozen.................................  2.80
     7,  ⅝    inch. Bore, 10   inch. long, each ....................  .55
    10,  ¾    inch. Bore, 11½  inch. long, each ....................  .65
    11,  ⅞    inch. Bore, 11½  inch. long, each ....................  .90
    12,  1    inch. Bore, 12½  inch. long, each ....................  1.55
    14,  1¼   inch. Bore, 14   inch. long, each ....................  2.60
```

Write for discount.

"Sparklet" Siphon

This Siphon enables you to make your own Seltzer Water at a cost or 4 cts. each.   You can also make Vichy and Lithia Waters.

Full directions accompany each Siphon.

Price, each ....$ 1.50

"Sparklets"

These Sparklets are for use with above Sparklet Siphon Bottle.

Price, per box of 1 dozen ....$ 0.75

Write for discount.

No 10—Cash Register

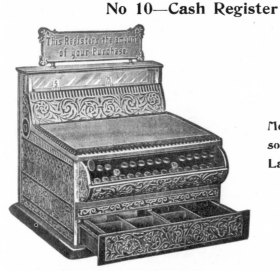

**Metal Case, Hand-
somely Nickeled,
Lacquered Finish**

Pushing the thumb lever cancels all former registration, uncovers keys, opens cash drawer and sounds the alarm.   The next sale must be registered before drawer can be closed. Detail adding machine, capacity over $2,400.00.

All operations automatic, all keys can be reset to zero, either simultaneously or singly.

All working parts metal.

Dimensions.   Height, 21 inches, width, 19½ inches, depth, 18 inches. Shipping weight, 80 lbs.

Price, each...$93.00

**Wood Cabinet,
Hard Oil Finish,
Highly Polished**

Same as above in every particular.

Price, each $77.50

Write for discount.

Latest Improved Sugar Swivel Bowl

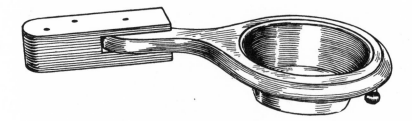

This is the most up-to-date Sugar Bowl known, having a granite agate bowl rendering it easy to clean as well as being much handier than the old style pull drawers.

Price, each...$ 3.25

Lemon Cutting Boards, each...................................... 1.20

Beveled Plate Glass Scratch Plates

Very convenient to put on counters to prevent customers scratching the counter to light matches.

Price, with Screws, 2½ x 10 inch., each...........................$ 0.50

Price, with Screws, 3   x 11 inch., each........................... .65

Extra for Silvered back, each .... .20

Write for discount.

Pedestral Siphon Filler

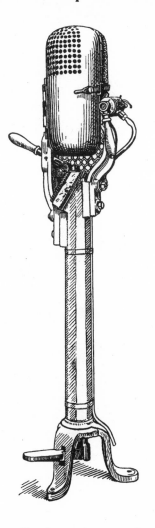

This Filler is indispensable where a large number of Siphons are used. The saving in time compared with the ordinary Siphon Fillers, will pay for the difference in price in a very short time.

Price, each $69.00

Write for discount.

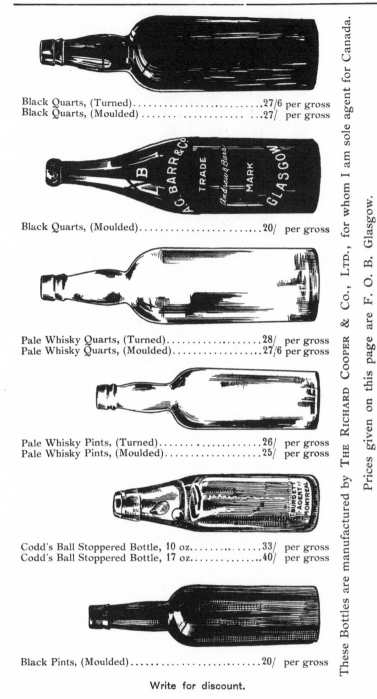

Black Quarts, (Turned)........................27/6 per gross
Black Quarts, (Moulded) ....27/ per gross

Black Quarts, (Moulded)........................20/ per gross

Pale Whisky Quarts, (Turned)..................28/ per gross
Pale Whisky Quarts, (Moulded)..................27/6 per gross

Pale Whisky Pints, (Turned)..................26/ per gross
Pale Whisky Pints, (Moulded)..................25/ per gross

Codd's Ball Stoppered Bottle, 10 oz.......... ......33/ per gross
Codd's Ball Stoppered Bottle, 17 oz.............40/ per gross

Black Pints, (Moulded)........................20/ per gross

Write for discount.

These Bottles are manufactured by The Richard Cooper & Co., Ltd., for whom I am sole agent for Canada. Prices given on this page are F. O. B. Glasgow.

Under Writer Fire Extinguisher

This Extinguisher has been on the market for years, and has proved itself to be equal, if not better than any Fire Extinguisher ever offered on the market.

Each Extinguisher is accompanied with a guarantee. It is superior to any Powder, as you can reach a fire at a distance of thirty feet. It is well recommended, as it is very seldom that a large institution does not file subsequent orders after once using the Extinguisher.

Price, each $28.00

Write for discount.

Bar Wood Arm Rail, Round

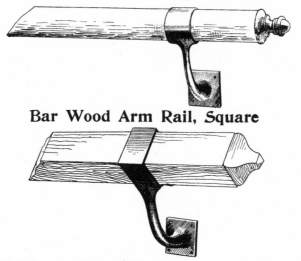

Bar Wood Arm Rail, Square

Polished Oak, Round or Square, 2½ in. diameter, per running foot....$ 1.50
  "   "   "   3   "   "   " 2.00
Brackets, Polished Brass, Round or Square, 4 in. x 5 in., each....... 3.00
Turned Knobs, Oak,   "   "   2½ in. diameter, each 1.00
  "   "   "   "   3   "   " 1.25

If plain Cotton wood, natural wood finish, is desired for any of these
wood Rails, price would be 15% less ; and if any other kind of hard wood is
required price will be the same as Oak. No extra charge will be made for
any particular finish which may be required for either soft or hard wood Rails.

Wood Towel Rail

Nickel-plated Brackets, each..$ 0.75
Rail, Ash wood, highly finished, per running foot .... .15
Turned Knobs,   "   "   each............................... .15

Nickel-plated Towel Rail

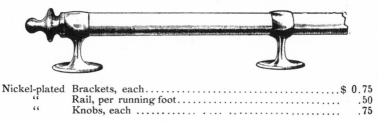

Nickel-plated Brackets, each..$ 0.75
      "   Rail, per running foot................................ .50
      "   Knobs, each .... .75

Write for discount.

Brass Foot Rail

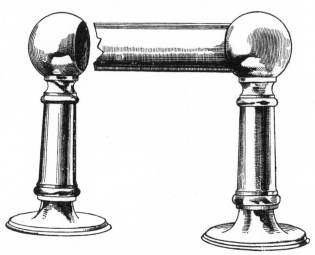

Posts for 1¼ in. Iron Pipe Size Brass Rail, each.........................$ 3.50
Rail, 1¼ in.   "   "   " extra heavy, per running foot. 1.50

The Posts are of a very handsome design, and are of the proper height, and can either be adjusted to the floor by means of screws or iron bolts.

The above quotations are for straight Rails ; if circular Rails are wanted price will be quoted on application.

Brass Door Guard Rail

Knob Brackets, per pair..$ 2.00
Rail, ¾ in. diameter, per running foot .... .45

Our Brass Rail is Iron Lined, which makes it much stronger than ordinary brass tubes.

Brass Bar
Arm Rail

Brackets, 5 in. x 4 in., each.......................................$ 3.00
Brackets, larger sizes quoted on application.
Brass Rail, 2½ in. diameter, per running foot 1.50
    "   3   "   " 2.00
Turned Knobs, 2½   "   " 1.75
    "   3   "   " 2.25
Nickel-plated Rail, per foot extra .... .75
Nickel-plated Brackets, each extra........................... .... .75

Write for discount.

The Cleveland Faucet Co.

Bung and Bush

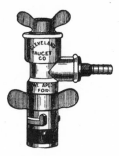

This style of Bung excells anything heretofore invented. It is simple in constructions and can be adjusted to the barrel by a child.

There is no parts to get out of order, and it is never necessary to remove the iron Bush in the barrel such as is the case with mostly all makes of devices gotten up to facilitate the tapping of Ale or Lager.

The Bush itself necessitates no special washers, an ordinary cork answers the purpose. Any ordinary tapping tube will fit this Bung. One foot of Beer Hose is sufficient to connect the beer pipe to the tapping tube. The saving in Beer Hose only, per year, will more than pay for three times the cost of each Bung and Bush.

Where this Bung and Bush are used the splitting of the barrel heads becomes a thing of the past, and this, without mentioning any of the above features, will save more than ten times the price of the Bush itself for each barrel.

Price on application.

Write for discount.

The Latest Improved Bottle Filler

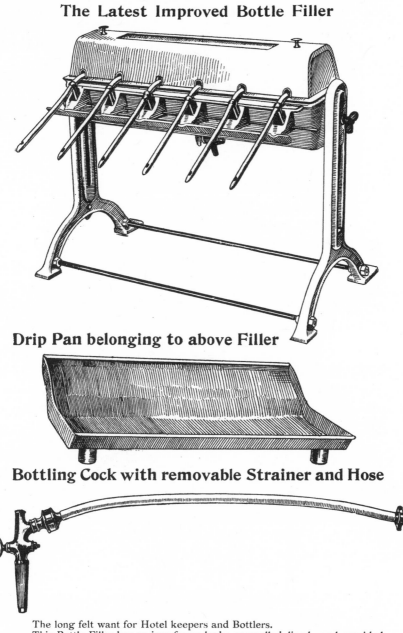

Drip Pan belonging to above Filler

Bottling Cock with removable Strainer and Hose

The long felt want for Hotel keepers and Bottlers.

This Bottle Filler has an iron frame body, enamelled lined, and provided with ball cock and automatic shut-off, also zinc cover with sight glass in same.

We supply these Fillers in sizes of 4 and 6 spouts.

Price, each, complete.................................. ....$75.00

Write for discount.

No 1310—Glass Holders

Made of the finest material, and outlast any other kind

Price, each ....$ 1.75

No 1311—Glass Holders

Price, each ....$ 1.75

No 1318—Glass Holders

Price, each ....$ 1.75

Write for discount.

The Champion Money Maker Outfit

O not pay 30 cts. per dozen for Ginger Ale, Cream Soda, Lemon Sour, Cider, etc., while you can make same yourself for less than 10 cts. per dozen, or pay $1.00 per dozen for Siphons when you can fill them yourself for about 10 cts. per dozen with our Champion Money Maker Outfit. This is not an experiment. but it has been tried, and the list of the purchasers, which will be furnished on application, should inspire enough confidence to any interested reader to take up the matter with us at once and write for further information.

For over fifty years several inventors have been experimenting to get up a system whereby an hotel-keeper could accomplish the manufacture of his own Ginger Ale, Cream Soda, Plain Soda, Lemon Sour, Mineral Waters, etc., but the great drawback was the cost of this machinery ; to-day modern science has found the Champion Money Maker Outfit which embraces all the points necessary to make it a success.

First—You make as good as can be made.

Second—You make them at less than one third the price you are paying for same.

Third—The price of the Champion Money Maker Outfit is nominal compared with the considerable saving you derive therefrom.

Fourth—You are not bothered with corks, or wire, as the Turnover Table shown on page 258, does away with this difficulty ; nor have you any syrup to measure, as illustration on page 197 clearly shows you the syrup pump which pumps the proper quantity of syrup required for each bottle.

This outfit has only been offered in Montreal since February 1st, 1904, and up to March the 8th, 1904, we could furnish thirty names of prominent hotel-keepers in Montreal and vicinity, who have purchased Champion Money Maker Outfits.

If you are skeptical as to the quality of goods you can make with this outfit, drop us a postal card, and we will send you by express samples of either Cream Soda, Cider, Ginger Ale, Mineral Waters, etc., and also give you the names of the purchasers of the Champion Money Maker Outfit, along with the price and conditions of sale.

The " Ideal " Turnover Table

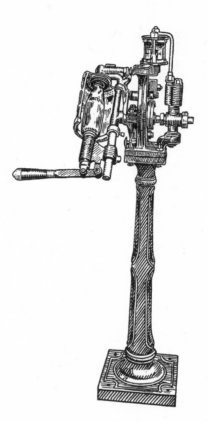

This Table is the same as illustrated on page 167, but shows the whole of the Stand.

This Table can be supplied also without the Stand where it is necessary to fasten same to the workboard, as in many cases the proprietor does his own bar tending and it is found very convenient to have the Bottle Filler behind the bar, as the bar tender can keep himself supplied with Ginger Ale, Cream Soda, etc., without leaving the bar.

Write for discount.

The Champion Money Maker Outfit

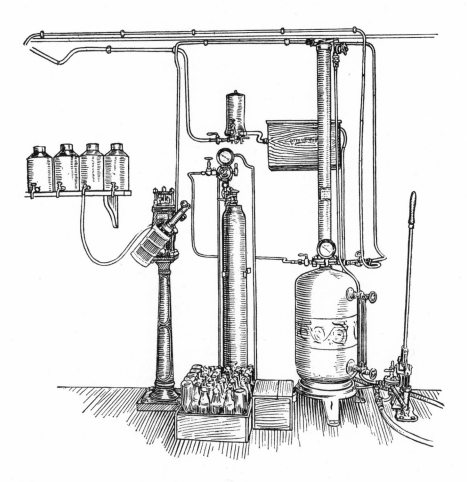

The best self-recommending Outfit and Money Maker ever offered on the market.

Specially adapted for Hotels, Saloons, Restaurants, and places where Ginger Ale, Cream Soda, Cider and other Aerated Waters are sold.

Write for discount.

"Little Wonder" Bottle Washer

Pat. December 15th, 1885

IMPORTANT TO BOTTLERS

This Washer is not an experiment—it is used by the largest Brewers and Bottlers in the United States and Canada. We have over 500 testimonials which speak in the highest praise of them—all of which came unsolicited—as the most economical, handiest and most effective bottle washer on the market. It washes any kind of a bottle that can be washed on a brush machine, doing its work thoroughly ; it is run by force of water from water works with a pressure of 40 lbs. or over. *It costs less than one dollar to put it to work when you get it, when any other make—even other kinds I make will cost from $25.00 to $50.00 to put them running, besides the price of the washer in the first place.* This is a great saving in trying a washer, which everyone likes to do before buying.

It sets on your tub or sink and takes the space of 12 x 30 inches. A jet of water 1-16 of an inch runs the whole machine. Water from motor goes into the sink, and being clean, is used again to wash off the outside and rinse the bottles, thereby using no more water than to wash by hand.

It costs 50 per cent. less than any other washer made for running expenses. Even if you have steam power in your factory this is the washer to have. Always ready, it is complete when you get it, and can be put to work in ten minutes after taking it out of box. Any part can be duplicated at short notice in case of accident. Over 3000 in use. Brushes are the best we can find after years of experimenting. *If you order give us your water pressure at your factory and kind of bottles you use, so we can adjust the washer to do the most good with the least expense.* Remember this.

Price, each......... ....$65.00

Write for discount.

TO WOMAN

Woman—Let us not forget that wherever man is most enlightened, she is most respected and beloved.

Woman—Gentle, patient, self-denying ; without her man would be a savage, and the earth a desert.

The Ladies—Always favorable to a *press*, properly conducted.

Woman—A Mistress of Arts, who robs a bachelor of his degree, and forces him to study philosophy by means of curtain lectures.

The Ladies—We admire them for their beauty, respect them for their intelligence, adore them for their virtue, and love them because we can't help it.

The Ladies—The honor of a lady is her name, and no legacy is so rich as honesty.

> May the blossoms of love never be blighted,
> And a true-hearted young woman never be slighted.

The Ladies—

> For though they almost blush to reign,
> Though love's own flowers wreath the chain,
> Disguise the bondage as we will,
> 'Tis woman—woman rules us still.
> They talk about a woman's sphere
>   As though it had a limit ;
> There's not a place in earth or heaven,
> There's not a task to mankind given ;
> There's not a blessing or a woe ;
> There's not a whispered yes or no ;
> There's not a life, there's not a birth,
> That has a feather's weight of worth—
>   Without a woman in it ?

Woman—She needs no eulogy—she speaks for herself.

Woman—The fairest work of the Great Author : the edition is large, and no man should be without a copy.

Here's to the maiden of bashful fifteen ;
    Here's to the widow of fifty ;
Here's to the flaunting, extravagant queen,
    And here's to the housewife that's thrifty !
        Let the toast pass ;
        Drink to the lass ;
I'll warrant she'll prove an excuse for the glass.

Here's to woman, whose heart and whose soul
    Are the light and the life of each spell we persue ;
Whether sunn'd at the tropics or chilled at the pole,
    If woman be there, there is happiness, too.

You may run the whole gamut of color and shade,
    A pretty girl—however you dress her—
Is the prettiest thing that ever was made,
    And the last one's the prettiest, bless her !

I fill this cup to one made up
    Of loveliness alone,
A woman, of her gentle sex
    The seeming paragon.
Her health ! and would on earth there stood
    Some more of such a frame,
That life might be all poetry,
    And weariness a name.

Drink to her that each loves best,
    And if you nurse a flame
That's told but to her mutual breast,
    We will not ask her name.

Drink to fair woman, who, I think,
    Is most intitled to it ;
For if ever anything could drive me to drink,
    She certainly could do it.

Here's to our sweethearts and our wives ;
May our sweethearts soon become our wives
And our wives ever remain our sweethearts !

Here's to the prettiest,
Here's to the wittiest,
Here's to the truest of all who are true.
Here's to the neatest one,
Here's to the sweetest one,
Here's to them all in one—here's to you.

Here's to the lassies we've loved my lad,
Here's to the lips we've pressed ;
For of kisses and lasses,
Like liquor in glasses,
The last is always the best.

Feminine grace, feminine goodness and feminine generosity ;
may they exist forever !

Here's to the girl that's strictly in it,
Who dosen't lose her head even for a minute ;
Plays well the game and knows the limit,
And still gets all the fun there's in it.

My woman, your woman ; but not everybody's woman.

A health to the maid with a bosom of snow,
And to her with a face brown as a berry ;
A health to the wife that looks eat up with woe,
And a health to the damsel that's merry !

A bumper to womankind, clumsy or thin,
Young or ancient—it weighs not a feather ;
So fill a pint bumper—nay, fill to the brim,
And let's toast'em, e'en all altogether.

The girl that is witty,
The girl that is pretty,
The girl with an eye as black as a sloe ;
Here's to girls of each station
O'er the Yankee nation,
And in particular, one that I know.

The wimmin !

So let us all ; yes, by that love which all our lives rejoices,
By those dear eyes that speak to us with love's seraphic voices,
By those dear arms that will infold us when we sleep forever,
By those dear lips that kiss the lips that may give answer never,
By mem'ries lurkin' in our hearts an' all our eyes bedimmin',
We'll drink a health to those we love an' who love us—the wimmin !

—Eugene Field's Toast to the Ladies.

Fair days, fair times, and fair ladies.

Friend, fill your glass, and then we'll part.
   Here's to the girl we love most dear,
Who, when no chiding tongue is nigh,
Breathing for us the midnight sigh,
   Her glowing cheek wet with a tear.
In fancy folds us to her heart.

Old wine and young women.

Here's to the girl that I love,
   And here's to the girl who loves me,
And here's to all that love her whom I love
   And all those that love her who loves me.

LOVE

Love—May it never make a wise man play the fool.

Lovely woman : man's best and dearest gift.

Love to one, friendship to a few, and good will to all.

May " Lovers' Vows " never end in " Lovers' Quarrels."

May we be loved by those whom we love.

May we kiss whom we please, and please whom we kiss.

May the confidence of love be rewarded with constancy in its object.

May the wings of love never lose a feather.

May the union of persons always be founded on that of the heart.

May the true lover never be deceived in the object of his affection.

May those who enter the rosy paths of matrimony never meet with thorns.

Our favorite girl.

Sincerity before marriage, and fidelity afterward.

The dignity of the fair sex.

The greatest blessing Heaven can send—a good wife.

> The ladies—God bless'em,
> And may nothing distress'em.

> Here's to those I love ;
>   Here's to those who love me ;
> Here's to those who love those I love,
> And here's to those who love those who love me.

—Ouida's Toast.

Drink to me only with thine eyes,
    And I will pledge with mine ;
Or leave a kiss within the cup,
    And I'll not look for wine.
The thirst that from the soul doth rise
    Doth ask a drink divine ;
But might I of Jove's nectar sup,
    I would not change from thine.

                                    —*Jonson.*

Here's lovers two to the maiden true,
    And four to the maid caressing ;
But the wayward girl, with the lips that curl,
    Keeps twenty lovers guessing.

The fairest work of nature—woman.

    Here's to you, my dear,
And to the dear that's not here, my dear :
But if the dear that's not here, my dear,
    Were here, my dear,
I'd not be drinking to you, my dear.

Here's a sigh to those that love me,
    And a smile to those who hate ;
And whatever sky's above me,
    Here's a heart for every fate.
Were't the last drop in the well,
    As I gasped upon the brink,
Ere my fainting spirit fell,
    'Tis to thee that I would drink.

                                    —*Byron.*

Here's to you two and to we two :
If you two love we two,
As we two love you two,
    Then here's to we four ;
But if you two don't love we two,
As we two love you two,
    Then here's to we two and no more.

Here's a health to the future,
  A sigh for the past ;
We can love and remember,
  And hope to the last,
And, for all the base lies
  That the almanacs hold,
While there's love in the heart,
  We can never grow old.

The world is filled with flowers,
  The flowers are filled with dew,
The dew is filled with love
  For you, and you, and you.

Fill the bowl with flowing wine,
  And while your lips are wet,
Press their fragrance into mine,
  And forget.
Every kiss we take and give
Leaves us less of life to live.

Let's be gay while we may,
  And seize love with laughter ;
I'll be true, as long as you,
  And not a moment after.

Here's to our wives and our sweethearts, and may they never
meet.

Here's to the man who loves his wife,
  And loves his wife alone.
For many a man loves another man's wife,
  When he ought to be loving his own.

Here's to one, and only one,
  And may that one be she,
Who loves but one, and only one,
  And may that one be me.

Here's to Love, a thing so divine,
  Description makes it but the less,
'Tis what we feel, but cannot define—
  'Tis what we know, but cannot express.

PATRIOTIC

OUR COUNTRY.

> To her we drink, for her we pray,
>   Our voices silent never :
> For her we'll fight, come what, come may,
>   The Stars and Stripes forever !

OUR NAVY.

> With the bulldogs of war
> Standing guard on our coasts
>   All fears of attack quickly vanish :
> Manned with hearts that are true
> To the Red, White and Blue,
>   They'll make all our foeman " walk Spanish."

A YANKEE TOAST.

The Boundaries of Our Country—East by the Rising Sun ; north, by the North Pole ; west, by all Creation ; and south, by the Day of Judgment.

Our National Birds,

THE AMERICAN EAGLE,
THE THANKSGIVING TURKEY :

May one give us peace in all our States—
And the other a piece for all our plates.
To the memory of

GEORGE   WASHINGTON,

The childless father of seventy millions.

THE MEANING OF U. S. A.

The U stands for the Union eternal,
The S for the Stripes and Stars,
The A for our Army undefeated,
The victor in a dozen wars ;
The U stands for our " Uncle Sammy,"
The S for our Ships in stern array,
The A for the Almighty One who guards us—
That's the meaning of U. S. A.

AMERICA.

My native land ! I turn to you,
    With blessing and with prayer ;
Where man is brave and woman true,
    And free as mountain air.
Long may our flag in triumph wave
    Against the world combined,
And friends a welcome—foes a grave,
    Within our borders find.

—*Morris.*

SENTIMENTAL

A health to our sweethearts, our friends, and our wives ;
May fortune smile on them the rest of their lives.

Adam's ale : and may so pure an element always be at hand.
All our absent friends on land and sea.
As we travel through life, may we live well on the road.
Happiness to those who wish it to others.
May our faults be written on the seashore, and every good action
prove a wave to wash them out.

Thus circling the cup, hand in hand, ere we drink,
Let sympathy pledge us, through pleasure, through pain ;
That, fast as feeling but touches one link,
Her magic shall send it direct through the chain.—*Moore.*

Here's to the tears of affection:
May they crystalize as they fall,
And become pearls, so in after years
To be worn in memory of those whom we have loved.

A mighty pain to love, it is ;
And 'tis a pain, that pain to miss ;
But, of all pains, the greatest pain,
It is to love and love in vain.

May those now love
Who never loved before ;
May those who've loved
Now love the more.

May the happiest days of your past
Be the saddest days of your future.

ELKS

All regular lodges.

All faithful and true brothers.

Every brother who keeps the key of knowledge from intruders, but cheerfully gives it to a worthy brother.

Every brother who maintains a consistency in love, and sincerity in friendship.

May every worthy brother be happy at night with his friend, his love, and a cheerful glass.

May all Elks be enabled to act in strict conformity to the rules of their order.

May the lodge in this place be distinguished for love, peace and harmony.

May the prospect of riches never induce an Elk to do that which is repugnant to virtue.

May every Elk participate in the happiness of a brother.

May every brother have a heart to feel and a hand to give.

May our conversation be such, that by it youth may find instruction, women modesty, the aged respect, and all men civility.

May we be more ready to correct our own faults than to publish the errors of a brother.

May every Elk have so much genuine philosophy, that he may neither be too much exalted with the smiles of prosperity, nor too much dejected with the frowns of adversity.

May we never rashly believe any report which is prejudicial to a brother.

May the conduct of Elks be such as to convince the world they dwell in light.

May every brother who is regularly entered be instructed in the morals of Elkdom.

May every brother use the mallet in knocking off those superfluous passions that degrade the man.

May we never condemn that in a brother which we would pardon in ourselves.

May hypocrisy, faction, and strife, be forever rooted from every lodge.

May all Elks go hand in hand in the road of virtue.

May love animate the heart of every Elk.

May every society instituted for the promotion of virtue flourish.

May no Elk desire plenty but with the benevolent view to relieve the indigent.

May all Elks ever taste and relish the sweets of freedom.

May the cares which haunt the hearts of the covetous be unknown to the Elk.

> Relief to all indigent brethren.
>
> To the secret and silent.
>
> To all the fraternity round the globe.
>
> The absent brethren of this lodge.
>
> To our next happy meeting.
>
> To all social Elks.
>
> To him who first the world began.

The heart which conceals, and the tongue which never reveals.
To all the brethren of this lodge, indigent or wealthy.

> Come, fill up a bumper and let it go round,
> May mirth and good-fellowship always abound,
> And may the world see
> That the B. P. O. E.
> Doth teach honest hearts to be jovial and free.

POLITICAL

Administration without peculation.

May the wings of liberty never lose a feather.

The sacred decree of Heaven—Let all mankind be free.

The ballot : the only mode of procuring a free and equal representation in Congress.

The politician who never turns his coat.

The cause of freedom all over the world.

The people : the only source of legitimate power.

Here's to America, the ruler and queen of the waves—May she always extend to the weak and oppressed those blessings with which her own sons have been blessed.

May our Senators be distinguished for their integrity.

The President—His rights and no more.

Our Country—May those who ill use her be speedily kicked off.

The American Constitution and the People—May the union, which age has cemented, be forever inseparable.

Stump Orators—May their footing give way when they utter falsehoods.

The Veto—May it never prove a sore *toe* to the people.

The American Eagle—May it never rise in anger, nor go to roost in fear.

Andrew Jackson's Motto—"Ask nothing that is not clearly right, and submit to nothing that is wrong."

Freedom from mobs as well as kings.

The Freedom of the Press—Truth published with honest motives and for justifiable ends.

America's Daughters—May the blue of their eyes, the red of their cheeks, and the white of their bosoms, be the standard of our love and patriotism.

18

May the honor of our statesmen, soldiers and seamen be without a stain.

> May Columbia's brave defenders
>   Ever stand for the good of her cause ;
> While such we can toast them, no rogues or pretenders,
>   Can injure our dear Constitution or laws.

Free discussion, and freedom from passion.

The Land we Live In—May those who dislike it find a worse one.

> To insure perpetuation
> To this great and happy nation,
> 'Tis the greatest demonstration,
> To give each generation,
> Of every rank and station,
> A liberal education.

Full stomachs, but no foul corporations.

Let us toast integrity, and roast corruption.

Peace and Purity at the Polls—The only conduct becoming freemen.

The Constitution of the different States—The bright stars which revolve around the great sun (the Nation)—May they ever respect the great centre planet that warms, lights and protects them.

May dishonest office-holders fall by a quick rotation of justice.

> Here's to Columbia, free laws, and a free church,
> From their blessings may plotters be left in the lurch :
> Give us pure candidates and a pure ballot-box,
> And our freedom shall stand as firm as the rocks.

May our chief magistrates and their cabinets form a government of unanimity, and from that basis defy a world of enemies.

Government places and patronage—May those who abuse either be kicked out, and may it be their last kick.

May every President of our dear union prove better, if possible, than his predecessor.

May the ships of America ever bear bright sails, good news, good cargoes and good hearts, and have fair winds and light seas.

Our Legislators—Sound hearts, sound heads, sound dispositions, and sound principles.

Our Governors—May they ever merit the esteem of the people, and be always ready to reward the deserving.

Our Chief Magistrates—May they always exercise their prerogatives for the happiness and welfare of the people.

Liberty—May it ever be enjoyed by Americans.

Our Statesmen—May they ever be endowed with the noblest quality of men—honesty.

May the eagles of monarchy never be suffered to build a nest in our land.

May every American, at his country's call, be ready to meet the foe.

May Americans share the sweets of liberty, and ever contend for the freedom and happiness of the human race.

America and her Children—Her sons are brave and honest, her daughters fair and modest.

May America ever be an asylum for the oppressed, and a school to teach them the great principles of republicanism.

> May those who'd be rude to American roses
> Feel a thorn's fatal prick in their lips and their noses.

Our Chief Magistrate—May the greeting which he has received from the hearts of the people be repaid by his faithful honor and fidelity.

Oblivion to party rage.

May party politics never corrupt principles.

Our Public Institutions—May it ever be the honest endeavor of each and every one of us to keep them as unblemished and untarnished as we received them from our predecessors.

Our Mayor—As vigilant and useful in his present station as any officer in the State, he is one of those upon whom we can look with pride, and say, "these are our jewels."

The Judiciary—As Sword-bearers to justice, we respect her administrators; though they often base their dicisions on common law, their's are no common minds.

The Citizen Soldiery of the United States—Ever ready to protect the link of the Union.

The Arms of our State—At all times the arms of the Union.

The Union—Now and forever, one and inseparable.

Machinery — The product of the mechanic — a source of the laboring man's wealth and happiness.

The Mechanics of the United States—The moving power of the nation.

Our Public Schools—Caskets containing our jewels; we look with confidence to our city fathers to see that they are rightly set.

Public Schools—The origin and the support of our republican institutions. They require the aid and encouragement of every patriotic citizen.

DRINKING

Merry have we met, merry have we been,
Merry may we part, and merry meet again.

A hearty supper, a good bottle, and a soft bed, to every man who fights the battles of his country.

A full purse, a fresh bottle, and a beautiful face.

A bottle at night, and business in the morning.

A friend in every glass—a mistress in every bowl.

Cheerfulness in our cups, content in our minds, and competency in our pockets.

Good wine and good company to the lovers of reasonable enjoyment.

May wine never prove the cause of strife.

May we act with reason when the bottle circulates.

May we always get mellow with good wine.

Good humor ; and may it ever smile at our board.

May our love of the glass never make us forget decency.

May we never be drunk at night nor dry in the morning.

May we bury our sorrows in a friendly draught.

May we always mingle friendship with the cup.

May we prize an old friend and love an old wife.

May we never see a frown in a bumper of wine.

May we—like the earth—drink deep and yet be thirsty.

May wine always be the whetstone of wit.

May we never be out of *spirits*.

May wine make cowards brave.

Sunshine and good humor all the world over.

The heart that fills as the bottle empties.

To our absent friends.

Three cheers for the man that first planted the vine.

The oftener wine is tasted may it be liked the better.

To our next meeting.

> Drink to-day and drown all sorrow;
> You shall, perhaps, not do't to-morrow;
> But while you have it, use your breath;
> There is no drinking after death.

To our social friends, all around the table.

> Here's to the glass we so love to sip,
>   It dries many a pensive tear;
> 'Tis not so sweet as a woman's lip,
>   But a d——sight more sincere.

Wine and Women—May we always have a taste for both.
Wine to strengthen friendship and light the flame of love.

Wine—The bond that cements the warm heart to a friend.

> I drink it as the Fates ordain it;
>   Come, fill it, and have done with rhymes
> Fill up the lonely glass, and drain it.
>   In memory of dear old times.

Let us have wine and women, mirth and laughter,
Sermons and soda-water the day after.

> > > *—Byron.*

> Here's to a long life and a merry one.
> A quick death and an easy one,
> A pretty girl and a true one,
> A cold bottle and another one.

> Here's to champagne, the drink divine,
>   That makes us forget our troubles;
> It's made of a dollars worth of wine,
>   And three dollar's worth of bubbles.

May the juice of the grape enliven each soul,
And good humor preside at the head of each bowl.

> The Frenchman loves his native wine;
>   The German loves his beer;
> The Englishman loves his 'alf and 'alf,
>   Because it brings good cheer.
> The Irishman loves his " whiskey straight,"
>   Because it gives him dizziness:
> The American has no choice at all,
>   So he drinks the whole d——business.

SPORTING

May the thirst of blood never disgrace an American sportsman.

May the end of the hunt prove the beginning of happiness.

May we never overleap the bounds of decency nor break down the fences of virtue.

May the pleasure of sportsmen never know an end.

May we always gain fresh vigor from the joys of the chase.

May the sportsman's day be spent in pleasure, and his night be devoid of care.

May every sportsman that worries his game be not only stinted in his pleasures but be accursed.

The true, jolly sportsman who looks cheerful as spring,

And thinks himself happy and great as a king.

May the heart of a sportsman never know affliction but by name.

May every sport prove as innocent as that of the field.

May the love of the chase never interrupt our attention to the welfare of our country.

May those who love the crack of the whip never want a brush to pursue.

May the lovers of the chase never want the comforts of life.

The clear sighted sportsman that sees his game with one eye.

The steady sportsman that always brings down his game.

The Hunter's Pleasures—The field in the morning, and the bottle at night.

MISCELLANEOUS

Life's three blessings : wife, children and friends.

Maids and bachelors married, and soon so,

Wives and husbands happy, and long so.

May we look forward with pleasure, and backward without regret.

May we always enjoy the end of a feast better than the beginning of a fray.

May every honest man make money, and be wise enough to keep it.

May our injuries be written in sand and our friendship in marble.

May we never know want till relief is at hand.

May we look around us with pleasure, and upward with gratitude.

May right overcome might.

May we live in pleasure and die out of debt.

May we always command success by deserving it.

May the best day we have seen be the worst we have to come.

May the present meeting be oft repeated.

May we never be angry or hungry.

May every liar be possessed of a good memory.

May we always do good when we can--speak well of all the world, and never judge without the fullest proof.

May every man be what he thinks himself to be.

May good humor preside when good fellows meet.

And reason prescribe when 'tis time to retreat.

May we never put our finger into another man's pie.

May no errors be found when our accounts are made up.

THE MUSICIAN'S TOAST.

May a crotchet in the head never bar the utterances of good notes. May the lovers of harmony never be in want of a note, and its enemies die in a common cord.

THE SURGEON'S TOAST.

The man that bleeds for his Country.

THE GROCER'S TOAST.

May we spring up like vegetables, have turnip-noses, reddish cheeks and carroty hair, and may our hearts never be hard, like those of cabbages, nor may we be rotten at the core.

The good die young.

THE HATTER'S TOAST.

When the rogue *naps* may the lesson be *felt*.

THE TAILOR'S TOAST.

May we always *sheer* out of a law-suit, and by so doing *cut* bad company.

THE BAKER'S TOAST.

May we never be done so much as to make us crusty.

THE LAWYER'S TOAST.

May the depth of our potations never cause us to let judgment go by default.

THE IRISHMAN'S TOAST.

Liberty all over the world, and everywhere else.

THE SCHOOL TEACHER'S TOAST.

The three R's—Reading, 'Riting and 'Rithmetic.

THE AMERICAN'S TOAST.

The memory of those who fought and bled with Washington to secure our glorious constitution. The glorious memory of our ancestors, who, in 1775, at Bunker Hill, shed their lifeblood to establish our liberty.

'Ere's to the 'ealth o' your royal 'ighness ; hand may the skin o' a gooseberry be big enough for han umbrella to cover up hall your henemies.—*Erminie.*

A good health to the boys far away.

Home—The father's kingdom ; the child's paradise ; the mother's world.

> While we live, let's live in clover,
> For when we're dead, we're dead all over.

Toast drunk by an Irishman during the cholera epidemic in India :

> Stand to your glasses steady
>   And drink to your comrade's eyes ;
> Here's a cup to the dead already.
>   And hurrah for the next that dies.

Here's to the four hinges of friendship—
Swearing, lying, stealing and drinking.
When you swear, swear by your country;
When you lie, lie for a pretty woman;
When you steal, steal away from bad company;
And when you drink, drink with me.

We come into this world all naked and bare;
We go through this world full of sorrow an care;
We go out of this world, we know not where,
But if we're all good fellows here, we'll be thorough-
                                        [breds there.

Here's to turkey when you're hungry,
    Champagne when you are dry,
A pretty girl when you need her,
    And heaven when you die.

The free press.

Here's to a bird, a bottle and an open-work stocking—
    There's nothing in this that's so very shocking—
The bird came from Jersey, the bottle from France.
    The open-work stocking was seen at a dance.

Here's to you as good as you are,
    And to me as bad as I am,
As good as you are and as bad as I am,
    I'm as good as you are, as bad as I am.

Some hae meat and canna' eat
    And some wad eat who want it;
But we hae meat and we can eat,
    So let the lord be thankit.

The girls we've left behind us.

A cheerful glass, a pretty lass.
    A friend sincere and true,
Blooming health, good store of wealth,
    Attend on me and you.

As we play our parts in the theater of life may we drink much
to make us act better.

Bacchus' blisses and Venus' kisses—May they ever be bachelor's fare.

Cash payments, and plenty of them.

Constancy and Love—May the one always attend on the other.

Death to the blue devils.

Envy in an air-pump, without a passage to breathe through.

THE DRUMMER'S TOAST.

> Fill, boys, and drink about;
>   Wine will banish sorrow!
> Come, drain the goblet out;
>   We'll have more to-morrow.

> We live free from care,
>   In harmony everywhere,
> Combined just like brother and brother;
>   And this be our toast,
>   The good " drummer's " boast;
> Success and good will to each other.

> May those that are single get wives, to their mind,
> And those that are married true happiness find.

May he who thinks to cheat another, cheat himself most.

May the man who does not love his country, neither live, die nor be burried in it.

May we be rich in friends rather than in money.

> Some men want youth and others health,
>   Some from a wife will often shrink;
> Some men want wit and others wealth—
>   May we want nothing but to drink.

> A little health, a little wealth,
>   A little house and freedom,
> With some few friends for certain ends,
>   But little cause to need 'em.

MIXED DRINKS

Whiskey Cocktail

Take 3 or 4 dashes of gum syrup.
2 dashes of bitters (Angostura).
1 wine-glass of whiskey.

Fill one-third full of fine ice ; shake and strain in a fancy red wine-glass. Put in a piece of twisted lemon peel in the glass and serve.

Gin Cocktail

(Use small bar-glass.)

Take 3 or 4 dashes of gum syrup.
2 dashes of bitters (Angostura).
1 wine-glass of Holland gin.
1 or 2 dashes of curacoa.

Fill the glass one-third full of shaved ice, and strain into a cocktail glass. Twist a small piece of lemon peel, place it in the glass, ahd serve.

Bottle Cocktail

To make a splendid bottle of brandy cocktail, use the following ingredients.

Take ⅔ brandy.
⅓ water.
1 pony-glass of Angostura bitters.
1 wine-glass of gum syrup.
½ pony-glass of Curacoa.

Champagne Cocktail

(Pint bottle of wine for three goblets.)
(Per glass.)

Take 1 lump of sugar.
1 or 2 dashes Angostura bitters.
1 small lump of ice.

Fill the goblet with wine, stir up with a spoon, and serve with a thin piece of twisted lemon peel.

A quart bottle of wine will make six cocktails.

Coffee Cocktail

(Use a large bar-glass.)

Take 1 teaspoonful powdered white sugar.
　　 1 fresh egg.
　　 1 large wine-glass of port wine.
　　 1 pony of brandy.
　　 2 or 3 lumps of ice.

Break the egg into the glass, put in the sugar, and lastly the port wine, brandy and ice.

Shake up very thoroughly, and strain into a medium bar goblet. Grate a little nutmeg on top before serving.

Rosco Cocktail

(Use small bar-glass.)

Take 1 tablespoonful of orgeat syrup.
　　 2 dashes of Angostura bitters.
　　 1 wine-glass of brandy.
　　 1 or 2 pieces of lemon peel.

Fill the tumbler one-third with ice, stir well with a spoon, and strain into a cocktail glass.

Manhattan Cocktail

(Use small bar-glass.)

Take 2 dashes of Curacoa or Maraschino.
　　 1 pony of rye whiskey.
　　 1 wine-glass of vermouth.
　　 3 dashes of Angostura bitters.
　　 2 small lumps of ice.

Shake up well, and strain into a claret glass. Put a quarter of a slice of lemon in the glass and serve. If the customer prefers it very sweet use also two dashes of gum syrup.

Mr. Dooley Cocktail

(Use small bar-glass.)

Take 2 dashes Angostura bitters.
　　 1 pony of brandy.
　　 1 pony of whiskey.
　　 1 pony of Vermouth.

Shake up well with two small lumps of ice ; strain into a claret glass, and serve with a quarter of a slice of lemon.

Automobile Cocktail

(Use medium bar-glass.)

Take 3 dashes of gum syrup.
2 dashes of Curacoa.
2 dashes of Angostura bitters.
1 dash of Absinthe.
1 pony of brandy.
1 piece of lemon peel, twisted to expressed
the oil.
2 small pieces of ice.

Stir thoroughly and remove the ice. Fill the glass with Seltzer water or plain soda, and stir with a teaspoon having a little sugar in it.

Martinez Cocktail

(Use small bar-glass.)

Take 1 dash of Angostura bitters.
2 dashes of Maraschino.
1 pony of Old Tom gin.
1 wine-glass of Vermouth.
2 small lumps of ice.

Shake up thoroughly, and strain into a large cocktail glass. Put a quarter of a slice of lemon in the glass, and serve. If the guest prefers it very sweet, add two dashes of gum syrup.

Brandy a la Hughes

(Use small bar-glass.)

Take 3 or 4 dashes of gum syrup.
2 or 3 dashes of Curacoa cordial.
The juice of half a small lemon.
1 small wine-glass of brandy.
2 dashes of Jamaica rum.
Fill glass one-third full of shaved ice.

Shake well, strain into a large cocktail glass, and fill up with Seltzer water from a syphon.

Whiskey a la Dayan

(Use small bar-glass.)

Take 3 dashes gum syrup.
2 dashes Orgeat syrup.
The juice of half a small lemon.
1 wine-glass of Bourbon, or rye whiskey.
Fill glass one-third full of shaved ice.

Shake well, strain into a large cocktail glass, and fill up with Seltzer or Apollinaris water.

Mint Julep

(Use large bar-glass.)

Take 1 tablespoonful of white pulverized sugar.
2½ tablespoonfuls of water, mix well with a spoon.
1½ wine-glass full of brandy.

Take three or four sprigs of fresh mint, and press them well in the sugar and water, until the flavor of the mint is extracted; add the brandy, and fill the glass with fine shaved ice, then draw out the sprigs of mint and insert them in the ice with the stems down, ward, so that the leaves will be above, in the shape of a bouquet - arrange berries, and small pieces of sliced orange on top in a tasty manner, dash with Jamaica rum, and serve with a straw.

Sherry Cobbler

(Use large bar-glass.)

Take 1 tablespoonful of fine white sugar.
1 slice of orange, cut up into quarters.
2 small pieces of pineapple.

Fill the glass nearly full of shaved ice, then fill it up with sherry wine. Shake up, ornament the top with berries in season, and serve with a straw.

Syracuse Brace Up

(Use large bar-glass.)

Take 1 tablespoonful of fine white sugar.
2 dashes of Angostura bitters.
4 dashes of lemon or lime juice.
2 dashes of Absinthe.
1 fresh egg.
1 wine-glass of brandy.
2 or 3 small lumps of ice.

Shake up thoroughly, strain into another glass, and fill it up with Seltzer water.

An Automobiler

(Use small bar-glass.)

Take ½ a lime or small lemon.
3 teaspoonfuls of raspberry syrup.
1 wine-glass of Santa Cruz rum.
3 dashes of Curacoa.

Squeeze out the juice of the lime or lemon into the glass, add the rind and the other materials. Fill the glass one-third full of fine ice, shake up well, and strain into a cocktail glass. If not sufficiently sweet, add a little more syrup.

Syracuse Pousse Cafe

(Use small wine-glass.)

Take one-fith Curacoa.
      one-fifth Benedictine.
      one-fifth Raspberry syrup.
      two-fifths fine old brandy.
      1 teaspoonful of vanilla cordial on top.

Brandy Scaffa

(Use small wine-glass.)

Take ½ fine old brandy.
      ½ Maraschino.
      2 dashes of Angostura bitters.

Brandy Champerelle

(Use small wine-glass.)

Take ⅓ fine old brandy.
      ⅓ Curacoa.
      ⅓ Benedictine.
      3 dashes Angostura bitters.

Whiskey Sour

(Use small bar-glass.)

Take 1 large teaspoonful of powdered white sugar, dissolved in a little Seltzer or Apollinaris water.

      The juice of half a small lemon.
      1 wine-glass of Bourbon or rye whiskey.

Fill the glass full of shaved ice, shake up and strain into a claret glass. Ornament with berries.

Hot Brandy Toddy

(Use small bar-glass, hot.)

Take 1 teaspoonful of fine white sugar.
      1 wine-glass of brandy.

Dissolve the sugar in a little boiling water, add the brandy, and pour boiling water into the glass until it is two-thirds full. Grate a little nutmeg on top.

Hot Gin Toddy

(Use small bar-glass, hot.)

Take 1 teaspoonful of powdered white sugar.
      1 wine-glass of Holland gin, or Old
        Tom gin (as preferred).

Dissolve the sugar in boiling water, add the gin, and pour boiling water into the glass until it is two-thirds full.

Cold Irish Whiskey Toddy

(Use small bar-glass.)

Take 1 teaspoonful of fine white sugar.
1 wine-glass of Kinahan's L. L. or
  Jamieson's whiskey.
2 wine-glasses of water.
1 lump of ice.

Dissolve the sugar in the water, add the whiskey and ice, and stir with a spoon. This is a delicious drink if made with either of the above brands of whiskey, preferably the first.

Egg Nogg

(Use large bar-glass.)

Take 1 large teaspoonful of powdered white
  sugar.
1 fresh egg.
½ wine-glass of brandy.
½ wine-glass of Santa Cruz rum.
A little shaved ice.

Fill the glass with rich milk and shake up the ingredients until they are thoroughly mixed. Pour the mixture into a goblet excluding the ice, and grate a little nutmeg on top. This may be made by using a wine-glass of either of the above liquors, instead of both combined.

Every well ordered bar should have a tin egg-nogg " shaker," which is a great aid in mixing this beverage.

Sherrry Egg Nogg

(Use large bar-glass.)

Take 1½ teaspoonful of fine white sugar.
1 fresh egg.
2 or 3 small lumps of ice.
2 wine-glasses of Sherry wine.

Fill the glass with rich milk, shake up until the egg is thoroughly mixed with the other ingredients. Strain the mixture into a large goblet, excluding the ice, and grate a little nutmeg on top.

Whiskey Fiz

(Use medium bar-glass.)

Take 1 teaspoonful of fine white sugar.
3 dashes of lemon juice.
1 small lump of ice.
1 wine-glass of Bourbon or rye whiskey.

Fill up the glass with Seltzer or Apollinaris water, stir thoroughly and serve.

Gin Fiz

(Use medium bar-glass.)

Take 1 teaspoonful of powdered white sugar.
3 dashes of lemon juice.
1 wine-glass of Holland gin.
1 small piece of ice.

Fill up the glass with Apollinaris or Seltzer water, stir thoroughly and serve.

Silver Fiz

(Use large bar-glass.)

Take 1 tablespoonful pulverized white sugar.
3 dashes of lemon or lime juice.
The white of one egg.
1 wine-glass of Old Tom gin.
2 or 3 small pieces of ice.

Shake up thoroughly, strain into a medium bar-glass, and fill it up with Seltzer water.

Golden Fiz

(Use large bar-glass.)

Take 1 tablespoonful of fine white sugar.
3 dashes of lemon or lime juice.
The yolk of one egg.
1 wine-glass of Old Tom gin.
2 or 3 small lumps of ice.

Shake up thoroughly, strain into a medium bar-glass, and fill it up with Seltzer water.

Gin Sling

(Use small bar-glass.)

Take 1 small teaspoonful of fine white sugar.
1 wine-glass of water.
1 wine-glass of brandy.
1 small lump of ice.

Dissolve the sugar in the water, add the brandy and ice, stir thoroughly with a spoon. Grate a little nutmeg on top and serve.

Whiskey Sling

(Use small bar-glass.)

Take 1 small teaspoonful of powdered white
  sugar.
1 wine-glass of water.
1 wine-glass of Bourbon or rye whiskey.

Dissolve the sugar in the water, add the whiskey and ice, stir thoroughly with a spoon. Grate a little nutmeg on top and serve.

19

Tom and Jerry

(Use punch-bowl for the mixture.)

Take 12 fresh eggs.
    ½ small bar-glass of Jamaica rum.
    1½ teaspoonful of ground cinnamon.
    ½ teaspoonful of ground cloves.
    ½ teaspoonful of ground allspice.
    Sufficient fine white sugar.

Beat the whites of the eggs to a stiff froth, and the yolks until they are thin as water, then mixed together and add the spices and rum, stir up thoroughly, and thicken with sugar until the mixture attains the consistence of a light batter.

Scotch Whiskey Skin

(Use small bar-glass.)

Take 1 lump of white sugar.
    1 small wine-glass of Glenlivet or Islay
        whiskey.
    1 small piece of lemon-rind.

First rinse the glass with hot water, put in the sugar, fill the glass half-full of boiling water, add the whiskey and stir. Serve with a spoon.

Irish Whiskey Skin

(Use small bar-glass.)

Take 1 lump of white sugar.
    1 small wine-glass of Irish whiskey.
    1 small piece of lemon-peel.

Proceed as directed for Scotch Whiskey Skin.

Tom Collins Whiskey

(Use small bar-glass.)

Take 5 or 6 dashes of gum syrup.
    Juice of a small lemon.
    1 large wine-glass of whiskey.
    2 or 3 lumps of ice.

Shake up well and strain into a large bar-glass.

Fill up the glass with plain soda water and imbibe while it is lively.

Milk Punch

(Use large bar-glass.)

Take 1 teaspoonful of fine white sugar.
    1 wine-glass of brandy.
    ½ wine-glass of Santa Cruz rum.
    Small lump of ice.

Fill with milk, shake the ingredients well together, strain into a large glass, and grate a little nutmeg on top.

Egg Milk Punch

(Use large bar-glass.)

Take 1 teaspoonful of fine white sugar.
1 wine-glass of brandy.
¼ wine-glass of Santa Cruz rum.
1 egg.
Small lump of ice.

Fill the glass with pure fresh milk, shake the ingredients well together, and strain into a large glass.

Claret Punch

(Use large bar-glass.)

Take 1 teaspoonful of fine sugar.
1 slice of lemon.
1 slice of orange (cut in quarters.)

Fill the tumbler two-thirds full of shaved ice, then pour in the claret until the glass is full, shake well, and ornament with berries in season.   Serve with a straw.

Sherry Punch

(Use large bar-glass.)

Take 2 wine-glasses of Sherry.
1 teaspoonful of sugar.
1 slice of orange.
1 slice of lemon.

Fill tumbler with shaved ice, shake well, and ornament with berries in season.   Serve with a straw.

Forty-First Separate Co. Punch

(Use large bar-glass.)

Take 1 teaspoonful of powdered white sugar,
dissolve in a little water.
The juice of a quarter of a lemon.
1 wine-glass of brandy.
1 wine-glass of Sherry wine.
Flavor with raspberry syrup.

Fill the glass with shaved ice.   Shake and mix thoroughly, then ornament with pieces of orange, pineapple and berries in season, and dash with Jamaica rum.   Serve with a straw.

Champagne Punch

(One quart of punch).

Take 1 quart bottle of Champagne wine.
3 tablespoonfuls of sugar.
1 orange sliced.
The juice of a lemon.
2 slices of pineapple (cut in small pieces).
1 wine-glass of raspberry or strawberry
syrup.

Ornament with fruits in season, and serve in Champagne goblets.

This can be made in any quantity by observing the proportions of the ingredients as given above. Four bottles of wine make a gallon, and a gallon is generally sufficient for fifteen persons in a mixed party.

A La Dayan Punch

(For a party of ten.)

Take 3 bottles of Champagne, iced.
1 bottle of Cognac brandy.
4 oranges.
1 pineapple.

Slice the oranges and pineapples in a bowl, pour the Cognac over them, and let them steep for a couple of hours, then pour in the champagne and serve immediately.

Syracuse Punch

(For a small party.)

Take 2 bottles of sparkling Catawba.
2 bottles of sparkling Isabella.
1 bottle of Sauterne.
2 wine-glasses of Maraschino.
2 wine-glasses of Curacoa.

Flavor with ripe strawberries. Should strawberries not be in season, add a few drops of extract of peach or vanilla. Ice in a cooler.

Under The Bamboo Tree Punch

(For a small party.)

Take 2 quarts of rye whiskey.
1 pint of Jamaica rum.
6 lemons, sliced.
1 pineapple, sliced.
4 quarts of water.

Sweeten to taste, and ice before serving.

Century Club Punch

Take 1 pint of old Santa Cruz rum.
   1 pint of old Jamaica rum.
   5 pints of water.

With the addition of lemon juice and sugar to suit the taste, this makes a nice punch.

The precise portions of spirit and water, or even of the acidity and sweetness, can have no general rule, as scarcely two persons make punch alike.

Wedding Punch

Take ½ pint of pineapple juice.
   1 pint of lemon juice.
   1 pint of lemon syrup.
   1 bottle of Claret or Port wine.
   ½ pound of sugar.
   ½ pint of boiling water.
   6 grains of vanilla.
   1 grain of ambergris.
   1 pint of strong brandy.

Rub the vanilla and ambergris with the sugar in the brandy thoroughly; let it stand in a corked bottle for a few hours, shaking occasionally. Then add the lemon juice, pineapple juice and wine; filter through a flannel, and lastly, add the syrup.

Sleeper

Take 1 gill of old rum.
   1 ounce of sugar.
   2 fresh raw eggs.
   ½ pint of water.
   6 cloves.
   6 coriander seeds.
   1 lemon.

Boil the cloves and coriander, with a bit of cinnamon in the water; mix together the rum, sugar, the yolks of the eggs and the juice of half the lemon; whisk them all together, and strain into a tumbler.

Locomotive

(Use large bar-glass.)

Take 1 tablespoonful of genuine honey.
   The yolk of a fresh raw egg.
   3 dashes of Curacoa.
   1 claret-glass of red Burgundy.

Heat the wine in a *thoroughly clean* saucepan until it boils, then pour it *gradually upon the other ingredients*, (which, previously, should have been thoroughly beaten together in a mug or pitcher), whisking and stirring the materials all the while, in order to prevent the egg from curdling. Pour the mixture into a large bar-glass, powder a little cinnamon on top, and add 2 or 3 cloves before serving.

This seems like taking too much trouble just to make one glass of Locomotive. The following proportions of ingredients makes four nice glasses :

Take 2 ounces of honey.
2 pony-glasses of Curacoa.
1 quart of high red Burgundy.
A few drops of essence of cloves.

Proceed as directed above, and serve in large goblets previously heated.

Sherry and Egg

(Use small bar-glass.)

Pour in about one wine-glass of Sherry. Then break in the glass one fresh egg.

Shandy Gaff

(Use large bar-glass or mug.)

Fill the glass half full of Ale, and the remaining half with Irish ginger ale.

In England, where this drink had its origin, it is made with Bass' ale and Ginger ale, half and half.

Half and Half

(Use metal or stone bar-mug.)

Mix half old and half new ale together.
This is the American method.

" Arf and Arf "

(Use metal or stone bar-mug.)

Mix porter or Stout, with Ale in equal quantities, or in proportions to suit the taste.

This is the English method, and usually, ''draw it mild, Mary, the ale first.''

Rock and Rye

(Use small bar-glass.)

Take 1 tablespoonful of rock-candy syrup.
1 wine-glass of rye whiskey.

Stir them together thoroughly, and serve.
This is often prescribed for a cold.

Stone Fence

(Use large bar-glass.)

Take 1 wine-glass of Bourbon or rye whiskey.
2 or 3 small lumps of ice.
Fill up the glass with sweet cider.

White Plush

(Use small bar-glass.)

Hand a bottle of Bourbon or rye whiskey to the customer and let him help himself.
Fill up the glass with fresh milk,

Gin Rickey

Take 1 lump of ice.
The juice of ½ lime.
1 wine-glass Tom Gin.

Fill glass with Seltzer water and stir thoroughly and serve.

Brandy Cocktail

(Use small bar-glass.)

Take 3 or 4 dashes of gum syrup.
2 dashes of Angostura bitters.
1 wine-glass of brandy.
1 or 2 dashes of Curacoa.

Fill the glass one-third full of shaved ici, shake up well and strain into a cocktail glass.   Twist a small piece of lemon rind in it and serve.

Improved Brandy Cocktail

(Use ordinary bar-glass.)

Take 2 dashes of Angostura bitters.
3 dashes of gum syrup.
2 dashes Maraschino.
1 dash Absinthe.
1 small piece of the yellow rind of a
lemon, twisted to express the oil.
1 small wine-glass of brandy.

Fill glass one-third full of shaved ice, shake well, and strain into a fancy cocktail glass, put the lemon peel in the glass and serve.

The flavor is improved by moistening the edge of the cocktail glass with a piece of lemon.

Vermouth Cocktail

(Use small bar-glass.)

Take 2 dashes of Angostura bitters.
1 wine-glass of Vermouth.
1 quarter slice of lemon.

Shake the bitters and Vermouth with a small lump of ice, strain in a cocktail glass in which the lemon has been placed. If the customer prefers it very sweet, add two dashes of gum syrvp.

Absinthe Cocktail

(Use small bar-glass.)

Take 2 dashes of Anisette.
1 dash of Angostura bitters.
1 pony-glass of Absinthe.

Pour about one wine-glass of water into a tumbler in a small stream from the ice pitcher, or preferably from an absinthe glass. Shake up *very* thoroughly with ice, and strain into a claret glass.

Brandy Smash

(Use small bar-glass.)

Take 1 teaspoonful of white sugar.
2 tablespoonfuls of water.
3 or 4 sprigs of tender mint.
1 wine-glass full of brandy.

Press the mint in the sugar and water to extract the flavor, add the brandy, and fill the glass two-thirds full of shaved ice. Stir thoroughly, and ornament with a half a slice of orange, and a few fresh sprigs of mint. Serve with a straw.

Gin Smash

(Use small bar-glass.)

Take 1 teaspoonful of fine white sugar.
2 teaspoonfuls of water.
1 wine-glass of gin.
3 or 4 sprigs of tender mint.

Put the mint in the glass, then the sugar and water. Mash the mint to extract the flavor, add the gin, and fill up the glass with shaved ice. Stir up well, and ornament with two or three fresh sprigs of mint.

Whiskey Smash

(Use small bar-glass.)

Take 1 teaspoonful of fine white sugar.
2 teaspoonfuls of water.
3 or 4 sprigs of young mint.
1 wine-glass of whiskey.

Proceed, exactly, as directed in the last recipe.

Gin Fix

(Use small bar-glass.)

Take 1 large teaspoonful of powdered white
sugar dissolved in a little water.
2 dashes of Raspberry syrup.
The juice of a quarter of a lemon.
1 wine-glass of Holland gin.

Fill up the glass two-thirds full of shaved ice, stir thoroughly, and ornament the top with berries in season. Old Tom gin may be used if preferred.

Santina's Pousse Cafe

(Use a small wine-glass.)

Take ⅓ fine old Cognac brandy.
⅓ Maraschino.
⅓ Curacoa.
Keep all the ingredients separate.

The Pousee was invented by SANTINA, who formerly was the popular host of a celebrated Spanish Cafe, in New Orleans.

Parisian Pousse Cafe

(Use small wine-glass.)

Take two-fifths Curacoa.
two-fifths Kirchwasser.
one-fifth Chartreuse.

Care should be observed to keep the ingredients from mixing together. See preceding recipe.

While Lion

(Use small bar-glass.)

Take 1 teaspoonful of pulverized white sugar.
½ a lime (squeeze out juice and put rind
in glass).
1 wine-glass Santa Cruz rum.
1 teaspoonful of Curacoa.
1 teaspoonful of Raspberry syrup.

Fill the glass half-full of shaved ice, shake up well and strain into a cocktail glass.

Brandy Sour

(Use small bar-glass.)

Take 1 large teaspoonful of powdered white
sugar, dissolved in a little Apollinaris or Seltzer water.
The juice of half a lemon.
1 dash of Curacoa.
1 wine-glass of brandy.

Fill the glass with shaved ice, shake, and strain into a claret
glass.   Ornament with orange and berries.

Egg Sour

(Use small bar-glass.)

Take 1 teaspoonful of powdered white sugar.
3 dashes of lemon juice.
1 pony of Curacoa.
1 pony of brandy.
1 egg.
2 or 3 small lumps of ice.

Shake up well, and remove the ice before serving.

Santa Cruz Fiz

(Use medium bar-glass.)

Take 1 teaspoonful of fine wite sugar.
3 dashes of lemon juice.
1 small lump of ice.
1 wine-glass of Santa Cruz rum.

Fill up the glass with Seltzer water from a syphon, or with
Apollinaris water, stir thoroughly and serve.

Brandy Fiz

(Use medium bar-glass.)

Take 1 teaspoonful of powdered white sugar.
3 dashes of lemon juice.
1 wine-glass of brandy.
1 small lump of ice.

Fill up the glass with Apollinaris or Seltzer water, stir thoroughly and serve.

Cold Brandy Flip

(Use large bar-glass.)

Take 1 teaspoonful of powdered sugar.
1 wine-glass of brandy.
½ wine-glass of water.
1 fresh egg.
2 lumps of ice.

Dissolve the sugar in the water, add the brandy, egg and ice, shake up thoroughly, strain into a small bar-glass. Serve with a little nutmeg on top.

Cold Rum Flip

(Use large bar-glass.)

Take 1 teaspoonful of powdered sugar,
dissolved in a little water.
1 wine-glass of Jamaica rum.
1 fresh egg.
2 or 3 lumps of ice.

Shake up thoroughly, strain in a medium glass, and grate a little nutmeg on top.

Port Wine Flip

(Use large bar-glass.)

Take 1 small teaspoonful of powdered white
sugar.
1 large wine-glass of port wine.
1 fresh egg.
2 or 3 small lumps of ice.

Break the egg into the glass, add the sugar, and lastly the wine and ice. Shake up thoroughly and strain into a medium sized goblet.

INDEX

A

PAGE

Absinthe Drip.. 44
Ale Lift... 201
Ale Strainer.. 201
Arm Rail, Wood & Brass...................................... 252 & 253
Artificial Plants................................. 224, 225 & 226

B

Back Bar Decanters....................................... 227
Bar Coats... 235
Bar Fixtures.................... 206 to 209 & 216 to 220
Bar Pitchers............................ 64, 65, 67
Bar Spoons.................... 31, 32, 33, 36 & 222
Bar Strainer.. 49
Barrel Funnel.. 48
Beer Hose Protector..................................... 113
Beer Measure... 46
Beer Vent... 240
Bitter Bottles.. 179
Bottle Caps... 109
Bottle Filler... 255
Bottle Holders... 94
Bottle Stoppers.............................. 95 & 180
Bottle Stands............................... 181 & 182
Bottle Tubes... 93
Bottle Washer... 260
Bottler, Home............................... 58 & 59
Bottles.................... 180, 227, 229 & 250
Bottling Cock... 255
Brackets, Rail.................... 72, 252 & 253
Brass Checks.. 112
Bung & Bush, C. F. Co.................................. 254
Bung Starts................................ 114, 240
Burner, Gas & Gasoline................. 102, 146, 147, 148 & 228
Butter Cutter... 106
Bystrum Lamps.................... 101, 102 & 103

C

Can Opener.. 103
Capping Machine... 232
Caps.. 109 & 153
Carbonators................................. 189 to 196
Cash Registers.............................. 238 & 247
Chafing Dish.. 119
Chair, Stool and Table................................. 239
Champagne Tap............................... 116 & 117
Champagne Tap Cutter.................................... 92
Champion Money Maker Outfit................. 257 & 259
Cigar Box Opener....................................... 118
Cigar Cutters... 91
Cigar Lighter............................... 96 & 97
Climax Strainer... 42
Coats, Bar... 235

PAGE

Cocks, Bottling .... 57 & 62
Cocks, Compression 61
Cocks, Liquor .... 56 & 62
Cocks, Plain Bib 61
Cocks, Racking 60
Combination Shakers .... 53 & 54
Cork Extractor 96
Cork Press 232
Cork Press & Capping Machine 232
Cork Pullers .... 9 to 16
Cork Screws .... 25 to 30 & 232
Corkee 205
Cracker & Cheese Bowls .... 69 & 99
Crown Openers .... 184 & 237
Crowning Tables .... 202, 203 & 204
Cup Strainer 42
Cuspidors and Spittoons .... 78 to 91

D

Decanters .... 183 & 227
Dice 98
Dice Boxes 236
Dice Top 236
Dipper Strainer 44
Dish, Chafing 119
Dishers, Ice Cream .... 118 & 222
Door Guard Rail 253
Drainers 150
Drip Cup for Urns 151
Drip Pan 255
Dynamo and Engine 242

E

Egg Separator 70
Electric Cigar Lighter .... 96 & 97
Electric Gas Lighter 221
Electric Lamps 221
Elgin Butter Cutter 106
Engines .... 242, 243 & 244
Excelsior Strainer 43

F

Faucets .... 63, 223 & 245
Filler, Bottle 255
Filler, " Ideal " .... 197 & 258
Filler, Siphon 249
Filter Bags 224
Filters, Noxall .... 186 & 187
Fire Extinguisher 251
Flask, Shoo Fly 180
Flowers, Artificial .... 224, 225 & 226
Food Warmer 120
Foot Rail 253
Forks, Oyster 33
Freezers, Ice Cream 234
Funnell .... 39, 40, 41, 45, 46 & 48
Furniture, Chairs & Tables 239

G

PAGE

Gas, Burners.................................... 146, 147, 148 &   228
Gas, Carbonating..   188
Gas Heater...   228
Gasoline Lamps................................... 100, 101 &   102
Gem, Spoons...   222
Glass Holders.................................... 34 &   256
Glasses .... 153 to   179
Grater, Nutmeg..   98
Graduate Glass..   229

H

Hazard Cup...   97
Heater, Gas..   228
Holders, Glass.................................... 34 &   256
Holders, Lid...   205
Holders, Towel.................................... 92 &   93
Home Bottler..................................... 58 &   59
Hose Nozzles...   113
Hose Protector...   113
Hydrometer & Jar.......................................   229

I

Ice Cream Dishers................................ 118 &   222
Ice Cream Freezers.....................................   234
Ice Cubator..   230
Ice Picks..   37
Ice Scoops...   110
Ice Shaves...   38
Ice Shredders.................................... 23 &   115
Ice Tongs..   231
Ice Water Pitchers.......................... 64, 65, 66 &   67
Ideal Filler.................................... 197 &   258

J

Jar, Straw...   228
Jiggers..   50
Jiggers, Funnel..   41

K

Knives, Lemon..   34

L

Lamps, Gasoline.................................. 100, 101 &   102
Leg Cork Screw...   232
Lemon Juice Extractor..................................   54
Lemon Knives...   34
Lemon Squeezers................................. 17 to 24 &   241
Lemonade Shakers................................ 51 &   52
Lemonade Straws..   179
Lid Holders..   205
Lime Squeezers...   24
Liquor Faucets................................. 63, 223 &   245
Liquor Measures..   46
Liquor Pump..   109
Liquor Thief...   109
Little Wonder Bottle Washer............................   260
Little Wonder Pump, Repairs............................   200

M

		PAGE
Mallets		114
Match safes		152
Match Scratches		248
Match Stands	72 &	78
Mats, Door, Cuspidor, Pitcher & Coin	76 &	77
Meal Auditor		176
Measures	40, 46, 47 &	48
Milk Urns		143
Mixed Drinks	283 to	288
Mixing Spoons	32, 33 &	36
Money Maker Outfit	257 &	259
Muddlers	35, 36 &	240

N

Novelty Back Bar Decanters	227
Number Plates	108
Nut Crackers	71
Nutmeg Grater	98

O

Oyster Forks	33

P

Pan and Plate Lifter		71
Papier Maché Trays		233
Pedestrial Siphon Filler		249
Pepper and Salt Shakers	55 &	98
Perfection Bottle Stopper		95
Pitchers, Ice Water	64, 65, 66 &	67
Platings		185
Poker Dice		98
Polish, Yankee Cleaner		111
Potatoe Masher	104 &	105
Pullers, Cork	9 to	16
Pump, Liquor		109

R

Rails, Arm, Brass and Wood	252 &	253
Rails, Brass Foot		253
Rails, Brass Door Guard		253
Rails, Towel, Brass and Wood		252
Registers Cash	238 &	247
Rubber Bottle Stoppers		95
Rubber Cushion for Glasses		153
Rubber Lemonade Shaker		51
Rubber Mats	76 &	77

S

Safety Pan & Plate Lifter		71
Salt Shakers		55
Sausage Cookers	66 &	70
Scoops, Ice		110
Scratch Plates		218
Seltzer Water Apparatus	198, 199 &	259
Shakers	51, 52, 53, 54, 55 &	98
Shredders	23 &	115
Sink Brush		236

PAGE

Siphon Filler.. 249
Siphons.. 176 & 246
Soda Apparatus...................... 189 to 196, 198, 199 259
Soda Bottle Holders.. 94
Soda Spoons............................ 31, 32 & 33
Sparklets.. 246
Spice Trays.. 68
Spittoons and Cuspidors........................... 78 to 91
Spoons........................... 31, 32, 33, 36 & 222
Spray Nozzle.. 113
Squat Bottle.. 229
Steak Pounders... 103
Stoppers, Bottle........................... 95, 180 & 240
Strainers....................... 42, 43, 44, 49, 222 241
Straw Jars.. 228
Straws, Lemonade... 179
Sugar Drawer... 248
Sugar Shakers.................................... 50 & 55

T

Table.. 239
Tongs, Ice... 231
Towel Holders................................... 92 & 93
Towel Rail & Brackets...................................... 252
Trays.............................. 67, 68, 74, 75 & 233
Tubes, Bitter.. 93
Tumblers..................................... 153 to 178
Tumbler Drainer.. 150

U

Urn Foot Rest.. 151
Urns, Hot Water, Chocolate, Coffee......... 121 to 133, 136 to 150

V

Vents, Wood Beer... 240

W

Water Coolers.................................. 134 & 135
Wine Bottle Display.. 182
Wine Coolers... 107
Wire Cutter.. 92
Wood Faucets.................................. 223 & 245
Wood Stoppers.. 240
Wood Vent.. 240
Workboards..................................... 210 to 215

Y

Yankee Cleaner... 111

Publications by Algrove Publishing Limited

The following is a list of titles from our popular *"Classic Reprint Series"*
as well as other publications by Algrove Publishing Limited.

ARCHITECTURE, BUILDING, AND DESIGN

Item #		Title
49L8096	☐	A GLOSSARY OF TERMS USED IN ENGLISH ARCHITECTURE
49L8137	☐	AUDELS CARPENTERS AND BUILDERS GUIDE - *VOLS. 1-4*
49L8016	☐	BARN PLANS & OUTBUILDINGS
49L8046	☐	BEAUTIFYING THE HOME GROUNDS
49L8112	☐	BUILDING WITH LOGS AND LOG CABIN CONSTRUCTION
49L8092	☐	DETAIL, COTTAGE AND CONSTRUCTIVE ARCHITECTURE
49L8015	☐	FENCES, GATES & BRIDGES
49L8706	☐	FROM LOG TO LOG HOUSE
49L8111	☐	LOW-COST WOOD HOMES
49L8146	☐	RADFORD'S PRACTICAL BARN PLANS - *OUT BUILDINGS AND STOCK SHEDS*
49L8139	☐	STAIR BUILDERS' GUIDE
49L8050	☐	STRONG'S BOOK OF DESIGNS

CLASSIC CATALOGS

Item #		Title
49L8098	☐	CATALOG OF MISSION FURNITURE 1913 — *COME-PACKT FURNITURE*
49L8097	☐	MASSEY-HARRIS CIRCA 1914 CATALOG
49L8079	☐	WILLIAM BULLOCK & CO. – *HARDWARE CATALOG CIRCA 1850*

GARDENING

Item #		Title
49L8082	☐	CANADIAN WILD FLOWERS (C. P. TRAILL)
49L8113	☐	COLLECTING SEEDS OF WILD PLANTS AND SHIPPING LIVE PLANT MATERIAL
49L8705	☐	REFLECTIONS ON THE FUNGALOIDS
49L8057	☐	THE WILDFLOWERS OF CANADA

HUMOR AND PUZZLES

Item #		Title
49L8106	☐	CLASSIC COWBOY CARTOONS, VOL. 1 (J.R. WILLIAMS)
49L8109	☐	CLASSIC COWBOY CARTOONS, VOL. 2 (J.R. WILLIAMS)
49L8118	☐	CLASSIC COWBOY CARTOONS, VOL. 3 (J.R. WILLIAMS)
49L8119	☐	CLASSIC COWBOY CARTOONS, VOL. 4 (J.R. WILLIAMS)
49L8103	☐	GRANDMOTHER'S PUZZLE BOOK 1
49L8142	☐	GRANDMOTHER'S PUZZLE BOOK 2
49L8150	☐	HERBIE WUZ HERE! (WWII CANADIAN WAR CARTOONS)
49L8127	☐	JOIN THE DOTS PUZZLE BOOKS
49L8081	☐	MR. PUNCH WITH ROD AND GUN – *THE HUMOUR OF FISHING AND SHOOTING*
49L8126	☐	OUR BOARDING HOUSE WITH MAJOR HOOPLE – *1927*
49L8125	☐	OUT OUR WAY–*SAMPLER 20s, 30s & 40s* (J.R. WILLIAMS)
49L8044	☐	SAM LOYD'S PICTURE PUZZLES
49L8084	☐	THE ART OF ARTHUR WATTS
49L8071	☐	THE BULL OF THE WOODS, VOL. 1 (J.R. WILLIAMS)
49L8080	☐	THE BULL OF THE WOODS, VOL. 2 (J.R. WILLIAMS)
49L8104	☐	THE BULL OF THE WOODS, VOL. 3 (J.R. WILLIAMS)
49L8114	☐	THE BULL OF THE WOODS, VOL. 4 (J.R. WILLIAMS)
49L8115	☐	THE BULL OF THE WOODS, VOL. 5 (J.R. WILLIAMS)
49L8116	☐	THE BULL OF THE WOODS, VOL. 6 (J.R. WILLIAMS)
49L8610	☐	THE CLASSIC ART OF HAND SHADOWS
49L8128	☐	THE NIGHT BEFORE CHRISTMAS WITH PUZZLE PICTURES
49L8107	☐	U.S. CAVALRY CARTOONS (J.R. WILLIAMS)

NAVAL AND MARINE

Item #		Title
49L8090	☐	BOAT-BUILDING AND BOATING
49L8707	☐	BUILDING THE NORWEGIAN SAILING PRAM (MANUAL AND PLANS)
49L8708	☐	BUILDING THE SEA URCHIN *(MANUAL AND PLANS)*
49L8138	☐	HOW SAILS ARE MADE AND HANDLED
49L8078	☐	MANUAL OF SEAMANSHIP FOR BOYS AND SEAMEN OF THE ROYAL NAVY, 1904
49L8129	☐	OLD SHIP FIGURE-HEADS & STERNS
49L8095	☐	SAILING SHIPS AT A GLANCE
49L8134	☐	SAILING VESSEL SILHOUETTES
49L8151	☐	THE ELEMENTS OF WOOD SHIP CONSTRUCTION
49L8144	☐	THE KEDGE-ANCHOR
49L8099	☐	THE SAILOR'S WORD-BOOK
49L8065	☐	THE SAILOR'S POCKET BOOK OF KNOTS
49L8058	☐	THE YANKEE WHALER
49L8025	☐	THE YOUNG SEA OFFICER'S SHEET ANCHOR
49L8061	☐	TRADITIONS OF THE NAVY

REFERENCE

Item #		Title
49L8024	☐	1800 MECHANICAL MOVEMENTS AND DEVICES
49L8055	☐	970 MECHANICAL APPLIANCES AND NOVELTIES OF CONSTRUCTION
49L8602	☐	ALL THE KNOTS YOU NEED
49L8083	☐	AMERICAN MECHANICAL DICTIONARY – KNIGHT VOL. I, VOL. II, VOL. III
49L8077	☐	CAMP COOKERY
49L8711	☐	DESIGNING SUNDIALS – *THE GRAPHIC METHOD*
49L8145	☐	HAWKINS' MECHANICAL DICTIONARY
49L8001	☐	LEE'S PRICELESS RECIPES
49L8135	☐	MUSSON'S IMPROVED LUMBER AND LOG POCKET BOOK
49L8019	☐	WINDMILLS AND WIND MOTORS

TRADES

Item #		Title
49L8014	☐	BOOK OF TRADES
49L8086	☐	FARM BLACKSMITHING
49L8141	☐	FARM WORKSHOP GUIDE
49L8087	☐	FORGING
49L8027	☐	HANDY FARM DEVICES AND HOW TO MAKE THEM
49L8054	☐	HOW TO USE THE STEEL SQUARE
49L8094	☐	THE YOUNG MILL-WRIGHT AND MILLER'S GUIDE

WOODWORKING AND CRAFTS

Item #		Title
49L8130	☐	50 POPULAR WOODWORKING PROJECTS
49L8147	☐	A COURSE OF INSTRUCTION IN WOOD-CARVING ACCORDING TO THE JAPANESE METHOD
49L8110	☐	CHAIN SAW AND CROSSCUT SAW TRAINING COURSE
49L8005	☐	COLONIAL FURNITURE
49L8065	☐	COPING SAW WORK
49L8032	☐	DECORATIVE CARVING, PYROGRAPHY AND FLEMISH CARVING
49L8710	☐	QUEEN ANNE FURNITURE - *HISTORY, DESIGN & CONSTRUCTION*
49L8003	☐	RUSTIC CARPENTRY
49L8052	☐	STANLEY COMBINATION PLANES –*THE 45, THE 50 & THE 55*
49L8034	☐	THE ART OF WHITTLING
49L8131	☐	TIN-CAN PROJECTS AND ART-METAL WORK
49L8042	☐	TURNING FOR AMATEURS
49L8067	☐	WOOD HANDBOOK – *WOOD AS AN ENGINEERING MATERIAL*
49L8060	☐	WOODEN PLANES AND HOW TO MAKE THEM
49L8013	☐	YOU CAN MAKE IT
49L8035	☐	YOU CAN MAKE IT FOR CAMP & COTTAGE
49L8036	☐	YOU CAN MAKE IT FOR PROFIT

Algrove Publishing Limited, 36 Mill Street, P.O. Box 1238, Almonte, Ontario, Canada K0A 1A0
Telephone: (613) 256-0350   Fax: (613) 256-0360   Email: sales@algrove.com   Web: www.algrove.com